Run Your Butt Off!

WORKBOOK

Run Your Butt Off!
WORKBOOK

Sarah Lorge Butler with Leslie Bonci, MPH, RD, and
Budd Coates, MS, the *Runner's World* running coach

© 2013 by Sarah Lorge Butler and Leslie Bonci

Printed in China

Rodale Inc. makes every effort to use acid-free ⊗, recycled paper ♻.

Book design by Christina Gaugler

ISBN 978–1–60961–596–3 paperback

6 8 10 9 7 5 paperback

We inspire and enable people to improve their lives and the world around them.
For more of our products, visit rodalestore.com or call 800-848-4735.

Run Your Butt Off!

Contents

Introduction

Run Your Butt Off! is based on the understanding that losing weight requires work. If it weren't so challenging, Americans wouldn't be confronting the weight problems they face today.

The human body is highly adept at storing fat, and once it has fat, it holds on tight. For most of human history, food was in short supply, so the body developed mechanisms to store extra energy in case of emergency. These days, we don't have to worry so much about days passing without nourishment, but our bodies still function as though we do. As a result, it takes a lot of effort to pry fat loose. We know it's not easy.

SLOW, SLOW, SLOW

Losing weight is not effortless, nor is it quick. Let's go over how fast the weight should come off: The National Institutes of Health suggests trying to lose $1/2$ to 1 pound per week. On the low end, that works out to roughly 2 pounds per month, or 12 to 17 pounds over the course of half a year. Remember this when you're setting expectations for yourself. RYBO isn't a crash diet. Instead, it's an introduction to a new sport and a new way of thinking about food, which will lead to gradual, sustainable weight loss.

A SIMPLE MATH PROBLEM

While losing weight may require some effort, the math behind it is pretty easy. In order to shed pounds, you need to burn more calories, or take in fewer calories, than your body uses in a day. Your goal is to create a calorie deficit.

There are three ways to go about creating this deficit.

1. You can eat less.
2. You can exercise more.
3. You can do both: Eat less and exercise more.

RYBO is focused on weight-loss strategy number three: Eat less and exercise more.

We call the nutrition portion of RYBO an "eating plan," not a diet. Yes, you'll have to monitor the food you take in. A little bit of running is by no means permission to park yourself at the all-you-can-eat buffet. But think of this as a self-guided course in educating yourself and changing your eating habits. Soon, you'll eat healthier (and less) without a constant, nagging sense of deprivation.

MEET THE EXPERTS

Leslie Bonci, MPH, RD, is director of sports nutrition at the University of Pittsburgh Medical Center. If anyone knows how to fuel a body in motion, it's her. You'll find her advice on eating in the pages that follow.

Budd Coates, MS, is our running coach. He has worked with beginning runners for more than 30 years and his "Budd's Buzz" tips throughout this workbook will help you stay strong and focused as your run your butt off!

Sarah Lorge Butler is the author of *Run Your Butt Off!* She's a runner who's passionate about the sport and you can thank her for gathering all this expert advice in one place.

Run Your Butt Off!

How It Works

The workouts to get you to your weight-loss goals aren't supposed to be grueling. Far from it.

This plan uses a gentle buildup. It starts with walking only, building up to 30 minutes at a time. The plan then includes some running. One minute at first. When you're ready, 2 minutes. Then 3, 5, 7 minutes. At a rate you determine, those 30 minutes of walking morph into 30 minutes of nonstop running.

The plan is presented in 12 stages. If you complete each stage in a week, you could be finished in as few as 12 weeks. In this book, you'll find enough daily journal pages to last you for those 12 weeks. Or you can opt to take it much slower than that. Repeat each chapter's workout for 2 or even 3 weeks, if necessary. Stretch out the whole process to take 6 months or longer, if you feel more comfortable doing it that way.

In other words, take as long as you need to become a runner. We've found that although it may take some time, once you're a runner, you will want to stay a runner.

Consistency will help you get there. When you begin exercising, you need to stick with it, week in and week out. You need to find time to work out at least 3—preferably 4—days a week, and keep that appointment with yourself. The repetition will make running easier. With that dedication over a period of weeks and months, you'll strengthen your cardiovascular system, which is responsible for pumping oxygen to the muscles. When you develop your heart and lungs, exercise feels better. And you'll be better able to nudge your body to relinquish its closely guarded fat.

YOUR UNIQUE CALCULATIONS

This plan asks you to do some basic math to learn more about your body and the calories it needs in a day. Weight loss happens when you eat fewer calories and burn more, so you need to educate yourself about where you are now, how many calories you'll have to cut to lose weight, and how your new exercise program will contribute to that caloric deficit.

This is a learning process. To succeed, you have to study a little bit up front. Many people start exercising, breaking a sweat for the first time in years, and they're offended when the weight doesn't melt off as fast as they think it should. They fail to reckon with how their eating habits are affecting their caloric total for the day. With a little math, you'll have a lot more knowledge. And with knowledge, you'll see results.

THE WORKBOOK TO MAKE IT EASY

This 12-week companion workbook will help you track your vital statistics: your weight each week, your calorie totals, and your workouts. With everything in one place, you'll be able to develop a plan for running and weight loss that makes sense for you. No one besides you has to see your personal data, but we firmly believe that when you have those numbers in front of you, you'll be equipped to make better decisions about eating and exercise. Plus, there's something satisfying about writing it down. It's always nice to put a check mark next to a task you've accomplished.

Get Moving!

This program isn't boot camp, and it isn't punishment. The last thing we want is for you to get discouraged during the first week.

We start slowly, build slowly, and run slowly. The weight might come off more gradually than if you took on a crash program, but doing it this way, the pounds are more likely to stay off. And you'll be a heck of a lot healthier in the long run (pun intended) by finding a routine you can stick with.

FINDING THE TIME

When you're introducing formal, regular exercise into your schedule, you need to build it into your day as if it were any other appointment, like a dentist visit or a parent-teacher conference, only more enjoyable. You don't blow off going to work every morning, nor should you skip your exercise appointment. If you don't organize an exercise timetable and instead leave it to chance, trust us when we say: Your workout is not going to happen.

Get your calendar (whatever form it takes) and figure out when you can find 30 uninterrupted minutes for exercise at least four times a week. You can use these workbook pages to schedule your workouts, too.

THE MAGIC OF FOUR

Do you need 4 days? Well, truth be told, 3 are okay, especially if you're exercising for the first time. But you'll see results so much faster if you can fit in four sessions. You'll be boosting your calorie burn over the course of the week with that extra session. And you'll start feeling better (breathing easier, moving easier, sleeping sounder) in less time. Best to schedule

4 days, with the understanding that if something unexpected crops up in your week, you have a 1-day cushion.

LOCATION, LOCATION, LOCATION

Do some poking around for a good spot to begin your walking—a route that is relatively flat is a smart starting point. Eventually the walking evolves into running, so you'll want to start off in a comfortable location. It's great if you live in a neighborhood where you can start moving straight from your front door, but that's not always feasible.

If you have to commute to your workout, look for parks that have walking or biking trails. Packed-dirt paths are ideal because that softer surface is forgiving on your feet, ankles, shins, and knees, but a paved path will do nicely. Either way, you don't have to stop for traffic, and if you're lucky, you'll have access to bathrooms and drinking fountains. Don't have anything like that where you live? Then look for a route with few traffic lights, so you don't have to stop while you're waiting for the light to change. Low traffic volume and wide shoulders on the road are big pluses, too.

Initially, walking and running can feel like a major effort to your lungs. Big hills will only intensify that feeling of work. Remember, we're trying to take small steps here. You can add the hills when you're a little more experienced.

Tracks can be a good choice if you don't get bored going around in a circle. They're flat, obviously, and the rubberized surface is gentler on your legs than asphalt is. If you're curious about the distance you've gone, you can keep track of your laps. Here's a hint: If you use a track, stick to the outside lanes until you're a much more experienced runner. Lanes one and two are for those who are doing high-speed intervals and trying to shave a few seconds off their next race. You don't want to get run over.

FIRST STEPS

When you have your exercise appointments scheduled and you've found a good place, you're ready to go. This program starts with walking. Before you can try running, you need to be able to complete four walks, each one 30 minutes nonstop, in a week.

How fast should you walk? Pick a pace that's comfortable—steady, not aggressive. Aim for a pace that's a little faster than your stroll-down-the-driveway-in-your-slippers-to-get-the-newspaper walk but slower than your might-miss-my-connecting-flight walk. Don't sweat the pace, just get out and do it. You do not want to be huffing and puffing. If you're panting, you're going too fast. Remember, this isn't punitive. You're not supposed to finish each workout feeling like you need a nap.

In the weeks ahead, as you start to integrate running segments into the workout, walking is going to be the recovery portion, the time when you take it easy and catch your breath. So if walking has you breathing heavy or unable to speak, your pace is too fast. Slow it down.

KEEP IT STEADY

As you move up to the running stages of the plan, you need to run slowly. Very slowly.

How slow is slow? Try this: Make your run no faster than your walk. Yes, that's right: no faster than your walk. You simply have to get running, so your body is airborne between footfalls.

MOVIN' ON UP

When it comes to torching calories, nothing beats running. If a 200-pound person walks a mile, he or she will burn about 106 calories. Run the same mile, and the burn is about 150. Plus, as you become more experienced, you naturally get a little faster when you're running, so you get more done in less time. Other sports can't keep up with running's burn, and neither can ellipticals or stairclimbers. According to the Mayo Clinic, jogging trumps swimming, cycling, weight lifting, and aerobics in terms of calorie expenditure.

Months down the road, as you develop into a runner, you can look forward to new worlds: new parks, new trails, new friends, and new races if you choose to enter them.

In the short term, you'll enjoy losing weight at a faster clip.

When you're just getting started, it's going to feel like a major effort. But even while you're exerting yourself, know what you're doing: Your heart is getting stronger, your lungs are breathing deeper. And the results aren't just on the scale. You may see your blood pressure, cholesterol, and triglycerides drop.

You're building muscles everywhere, especially in your legs, but also in your core due to all your deep breathing. You're increasing bone density. Then there are the "soft" benefits: the calm, the sense of achievement, the sounder sleep at night.

STICK WITH IT

It's common with new runners and exercisers that something happens to subvert their week, and they fall off the wagon. Maybe it's the flu, maybe it's a work deadline, maybe it's an unexpected trip out of state to look in on your elderly aunt. You don't get your three or four workouts in.

Its a mistake to try to climb back on the wagon at the exact same place where you fell off or, worse, to try to increase the intensity without having done your homework. Make sure you've laid the groundwork before you try to increase the running interval. When you're ready, then take it up a notch.

STRETCH IT OUT

You'll notice that each stage of the RYBO program begins with a walk. This is a warmup, and it prepares your muscles, heart, and lungs for the more demanding periods of running that are part of each workout.

Some beginning runners like to stretch even before they walk. Do you have to stretch? It's up to you. It's important to remember, however, not to stretch cold muscles, because you risk injuring yourself. It's best to get moving with an active warmup, or "dynamic" stretching. Save your "static" stretching for when you're finished with your workout and your muscles are warm. Learn more about stretching in Chapter 3 of *Run Your Butt Off!*

EXTRA CREDIT

If you're used to doing other activity, keep it up! The more active you are, the more calories you burn. Don't think that just because you're starting to run, you have to quit all your other activities. Runners just call other sports cross-training, and they're good for you. They work muscle groups that you might not hit with running and give you a mental break in your routine when you have something different to anticipate. Plus, you might notice that walking and running will help those endeavors.

TRICKS OF THE TREADMILL

Ideally, you're getting outside for your runs, breathing in fresh air, noticing birds and flowers, and chatting with your friends. But if you're running indoors on a treadmill, that's okay, too.

Beginning runners often wonder whether they get the same workout on a treadmill as they do outdoors. It's easier for your foot to push off a treadmill than it is, say, a dirt path. You don't have to deal with wind resistance. Sometimes it feels easier. To which we say, "Who cares?" At the beginning runner level, it's perfectly fine to substitute a treadmill workout for your regularly scheduled outdoor workout.

Here's the problem, though. Beginners get caught up in the data on the console: the calories burned, the miles covered, the speed. At this stage in your development as a runner, it's not healthy to fixate on the numbers. Ignore them!

FRIEND REQUEST

More than any piece of equipment, what's the one thing that's really going to help you stick with this program? A buddy.

Knowing a friend is out there waiting for you can make all the difference between hitting the "snooze" button and getting out of bed.

THE RACE IS ON!

Really want to jump-start your motivation? Sign up for a race.

Don't sign up for one happening this weekend. It shouldn't be next weekend, either. It could be a month from now or in 4 months or even a year, but start scouting. Pick a 5-K (which is 3.1 miles) and get it on your calendar.

When that race is on your calendar, suddenly you'll be more focused in your training. You'll keep pushing to see what you can do instead of finding a comfortable level and coasting along for a few weeks. After all, you have a deadline to meet—a race. Also, you'll find even more impetus to get out of bed and train. You don't want to try to fake it through a 5-K when you have a bib number pinned to your shirt.

ACHES AND PAINS

If you're doing everything as we've prescribed—building up gradually, taking it slowly, giving yourself a day off between most workouts, wearing supportive shoes—you should be good to keep going. But if you find yourself with new pain, ask yourself a few questions.

Are you tired, or hurt? Tired is not a bad thing, and sometimes when you get yourself out the door, you feel completely revitalized a few minutes later. If the flattened-by-a-steamroller feeling doesn't dissipate after 10 or 15 minutes, bag it and try again tomorrow.

When it's pain, is it running-related pain? Is it new? Does it get worse with running? Proceed with caution if the answer to any of these questions is yes. Usually, the garden-variety getting-into-shape twinges ease during the off day after a run. If they don't, give yourself an additional day or two off. If you still feel a sharp pain on the 4th day after a run, that's when it's time to call a doctor. Look for a sports medicine specialist who runs.

Run Your Butt Off!

Start Losing!

Here's what we know: A pound of fat is equivalent to about 3,500 calories. Consume 3,500 more calories than your body can use, and you'll gain a pound. That's the calculation the media use when you see those headlines: "Extra! Extra! If You Overeat by 100 Calories a Day, You'll Gain 10 Pounds a Year!" (That's correct, by the way.)

HOW MANY CALORIES DO YOU NEED?

By making some preliminary calculations about the calories your body uses in a day, you'll get a much more accurate picture of what you need to do to lose weight.

This basic rate of calorie burn—what you burn when you're at rest—is called your basal metabolic rate, or BMR for short. Everyone has a different BMR. The number changes depending on how big you are to start with and how much of your size is muscle or fat.

We've built a calculator you can use at runnersworld.com/rybo.

Enter your number, in pencil, below.

My BMR: __1,686__

Why in pencil? As you lose weight, your BMR—the number of calories you need in a day to function at rest—goes down, too.

Of course, few of us are entirely sedentary. We're walking around the house, climbing stairs, standing in line at the post office, lifting kids in and out of their car seats, pushing a cart through a grocery store, unloading the groceries and putting them away, folding laundry. And maybe your job

requires some standing and walking around. So you get to add a little bit to your BMR. Because, of course, any physical activity beyond lying in bed burns extra calories.

How much? Try the Harris-Benedict equation. Once you get your BMR, multiply it by a factor ranging from 1.2 (sedentary) to 1.9 (lumberjack), depending on how much activity you get during the day. There are five activity levels on the scale.

➤ If you are sedentary, multiply your BMR × 1.2.

➤ If you are lightly active, multiply your BMR × 1.375.

➤ If you are moderately active, multiply your BMR × 1.55. ✓

➤ If you are very active, multiply your BMR × 1.725.

➤ If you are extra active, multiply your BMR × 1.9.

Take your BMR, multiply it by one of the Harris-Benedict factors, and enter it here.

My total calorie needs: _2,023_

This is the number of calories you need to maintain your current weight. Ideally, you should be eating about that number every day. If you eat more than your total calorie needs, you will gain weight. It may be a slow creep, but you'll be gaining. You have to get to neutral before you can start to think about losing. But don't drive yourself crazy calculating calories to the decimal point.

BEGIN THE BURN

A pound of fat is about 3,500 calories. So to lose a pound a week, which is the upper end of the range of what the National Institutes of Health says is reasonable, you have to create a caloric deficit of about **500 calories per day.**

It's hard to say exactly how many calories you'll use on the workouts, because it does depend somewhat on your intensity. In the time it takes for one person to cover 2 miles, another person might make it only 1½ miles. But we can give you an estimate based on a 2004 study called "Energy Expenditure of Walking and Running" by researchers at Syracuse University. Take your body weight in pounds and multiply it by 0.53. That gives you the calories you burn walking 1 mile. For running, you can use 0.75 times your weight in pounds to give you calories used.

Calories Burned Per Mile Walking or Running

IF YOU WEIGH:	AND YOU WALK . . .			AND YOU RUN (THE ENTIRE WAY) . . .		
	1 MILE	2 MILES	3 MILES	1 MILE	2 MILES	3 MILES
120	63.6	127.2	190.8	90	180	270
130	68.9	137.8	206.7	97.5	195	292.5
140	74.2	148.4	222.6	105	210	315
150	79.5	159	238.5	112.5	225	337.5
160	84.8	169.6	254.4	120	240	360
170	90.1	180.2	270.3	127.5	255	382.5
180	95.4	190.8	286.2	135	270	405
190	100.7	201.4	302.1	142.5	285	427.5
200	106	212	318	150	300	450
210	111.3	222.6	333.9	157.5	315	472.5
220	116.6	233.2	349.8	165	330	495
230	121.9	243.8	365.7	173.5	345	517.5
240	127.2	254.4	381.6	180	360	540
250	132.5	265	397.5	187.5	375	562.5
260	137.8	275.6	413.4	195	390	585
270	143.1	286.2	429.3	202.5	405	607.5
280	148.4	296.8	445.2	210	420	630
290	153.7	307.4	461.1	217.5	435	652.5
300	159	318	477	225	450	675

Calculations based on Cameron, et al., "Energy Expenditure of Walking and Running." Medicine and Science in Sport and Exercise, December 2004.

It's kind of sobering to think that in the 60 seconds or so it takes you to eat a glazed doughnut, you can completely negate the calories you burned (and then some) during a half-hour workout.

But it's good that you know it for three reasons. First, that knowledge will give you motivation to stay away from the doughnuts. Second, you can be realistic about what you need to do to lose weight. Third, you realize that you can't eat anything you want just because you're exercising.

Again, to lose a pound a week, you need to create a deficit of about 500 calories per day. Reasonable weight loss is $\frac{1}{2}$ to 1 pound per week. That works out to somewhere between 2 and 4 pounds per month. If you're okay with losing $\frac{1}{2}$ pound a week, you'll need a deficit only half that size, or 250 calories per day. Realize, though, that early on the best way for you to create that calorie deficit is by changing your eating habits. Which, by the way, does not excuse you from exercising!

At the beginning, when you're mostly walking, exercise provides a relatively small proportion of the calorie deficit you create. Stick with it, though. As you go through the program and gradually start running more, you'll burn more and more calories with each workout.

MEAL TIMING IS EVERYTHING

Many of us are so busy during the day that we don't eat enough. When we finally do have time to eat at night, it's off to the races, finishing dinner then scavenging in the cupboards, fridge, and freezer.

In an ideal world you'd have three meals, each about the same size. Breakfast is maybe a little smaller, dinner maybe a little bigger. Then you get a decent-size snack, either in the afternoon if you're eating dinner late, or in the evening if you've eaten dinner early. A second small snack, if necessary, can tide you over between breakfast and lunch.

But when you only eat little nibbles throughout the day, you're exhausted from hunger. And then you're setting yourself up to overdo it with a giant meal at night.

HOW THE TIMING LOOKS ON A GOOD DAY

Here are two possible timing scenarios for a sensible day of eating. Obviously, you can adjust them to fit your schedule, but you can see how the meals occur at regular intervals throughout the day.

Changing the timing of what you eat can be tough to get used to at first. If you're not accustomed to a big breakfast, it can take several days to build up to it. When you're used to constantly snacking throughout the day and you instead try to aggregate your eating into three meals and a snack, you might find yourself experiencing hunger pangs at those times when you used to grab a handful of pretzels.

Scenario 1

7:00 A.M.	**Breakfast**
10:00 A.M.	Small snack, if necessary
12 NOON (or 1:00 P.M.)	**Lunch** (later if you had a morning snack)
4:00 P.M.	Snack
8:00 P.M.	**Dinner**

Scenario 2

7:00 A.M.	**Breakfast**
10:00 A.M.	Small snack, if necessary
12 NOON (or 1:00 P.M.)	**Lunch** (later if you had a morning snack)
5:30 P.M.	**Dinner**
9:30 P.M.	Snack

The goal is to eat when you're hungry but not starving, so you don't overdo it in one sitting. No doubt fine-tuning the timing and the quantities will be a work in progress for a couple of weeks. But likely you'll find that you consume fewer total calories throughout the day. And that's what you need to do to shed weight: The calories you burn must exceed the calories you take in each day.

TRAIN YOUR BRAIN

Many of the fad diets that have been popular over the past 30 years have completely eliminated a particular type of food or food group or overloaded on a strange ingredient. First everything was fat free. Then there was the oat bran craze. Carbs got the boot when Atkins came along. The only thing that all these plans had in common? People didn't have to think. They could just keep shoveling in the calories as long as they were eating or avoiding the one item that each particular diet zeroed in on.

Look, you need to train the muscle between your ears as much as you do your stomach and legs. You have to think this through if you're going to be able to make the choices that will help you lose weight. RYBO, remember, is about education, not deprivation. When you're at the store, you have to do the flip-and-read—the glance at the label—to understand what you're getting.

THE POSTWORKOUT SNACK

By filling up the tank with a satisfying postrun snack, you'll be better able to stave off the munchies that hit later. If you're the type who finds that running makes you hungry, try to eat within 30 minutes of finishing your workout. Aim for a balance of healthy carbohydrates and protein, which will make you feel satisfied. First drink water to give your stomach the feeling of "yes, there's something in there."

COUNT PROTEIN FIRST, THEN CALORIES

By adding the right kind of protein to your diet along with plenty of fruits and veggies, your calorie total for the day will naturally fall in line. If you eat enough protein, you won't be as hungry. And trust me when I say that it's more fun to make sure you're getting enough of something than to hold back from consuming too much. Addition is great; restriction is annoying. As for tracking your calories, we recommend using a Web site like calorieking.com. You can also try choosemyplate.gov, which has a SuperTracker to calculate calorie input and output.

A WORD ON HUNGER

Is it possible to lose weight without being hungry? How much sacrifice do we have to make, and how uncomfortable do we have to feel, to shed the pounds?

Like anything, it depends on the person. It depends on what habits we had going into this and how much we have to change. Plus, everyone has a different perception of hunger.

Here's some good news, however: People who are trying to shed pounds don't want to let themselves get extremely hungry, because then they run the risk of overcompensating and overdoing it when they encounter food again. Listen to your inner hunger-ometer: 1 is starving—10 is stuffed. Eat when you are at a tolerable 3 or 4 rather than waiting until you are starving (at a 1 or 2). The converse applies, too: You don't want to eat until you're absolutely stuffed. Try eating until you're a comfortable 7 or 8, not a jam-packed, can't-possibly-fit-another-bite 9 or 10.

Leslie's 12 Rules for Weight-Loss Success

1. LOG IT! Write down everything you eat for 1 week. A log gives you an unflinching look at your calorie consumption. With this record, you can examine your habits to see what eating patterns are sabotaging your weight-loss efforts.

2. SPACE IT! Eat at regular 4- to 5-hour intervals throughout the day. Don't wait to eat until you're starving, but do give your body some time off from eating during the day. The strategy of "grazing" often does not work for people trying to lose weight. Eat breakfast every day. An evening snack can be fine, especially if you eat dinner early, stay up late, or work out in the evening.

3. MEASURE IT! Leave your measuring spoons and cups out so you remember to use them. Get in the habit of measuring cereal, rice and pasta, juice, salad dressing, and other items that don't come in single-serving sizes. Often we allot ourselves much more than a serving. It takes a while to train the eyes and brain to recognize what a real serving size is.

4. SHOP IT! Plan a week's worth of meals, check what ingredients you have on hand, and make a comprehensive shopping list. When you get to the store, stick to your list. This will save you time and money. If you load your cart with a mix of nutrient-rich foods, including produce, low-fat dairy products, lean meats, and whole grains, the cart won't have room for junk food.

5. SLOW IT DOWN! Chew your food and taste it. Put your fork down between bites. Turn off the TV so you're

concentrating on your meal. Talk to your mealtime companions. Try to take 20 minutes per meal. This gives the nerve endings in the digestive tract enough time to signal the brain that you're full. Slowing down prevents overeating.

6. COLOR IT! Add one red, yellow, orange, green, or purple food to every meal. Making sure you get fruits or vegetables with each meal will help give your body the vitamins, minerals, and fiber it needs. You'll also feel fuller.

7. MUSCLE IT! Eat some protein at every meal. Aim to get ½ gram of protein per pound of body weight in a day. Protein preserves and builds muscle mass and makes you feel satisfied. And your body works harder digesting protein, which burns more calories.

8. DRINK IT! Women need 90 ounces of fluid each day; men need 125 ounces. As long as it's not alcohol, any liquid counts toward the total. With every meal, drink a glass of water. Coffee, tea, broth, and even the liquid in fruits and vegetables also contribute to the fluid you need.

9. SWAP IT! Look for healthy swaps you can make, like buying bread with more fiber and selecting lower-fat dairy products and leaner meat. These painless swaps can cut calories and add more nutrients to your diet.

10. SEASON IT! Honor your taste buds. Using herbs, spices, seasoning mixes, and flavorings is an easy way to give healthy foods an extra kick. If your mouth gets bored, you're more likely to experience cravings, which can sabotage your healthy eating.

11. FINE-TUNE IT! Log your food intake again and figure out what parts of your diet have improved—and where you still need to devote some attention.

12. THINK IT THROUGH! Anticipate those situations, like restaurant dining or weekend events, that might challenge your resolve to eat well. Plan for how you can enjoy special occasions without overeating. Examine your mind-set and avoid the "I've blown it" mentality. People get into trouble when they feel like a large meal or unhealthy treat wrecks their diet, so they might as well continue to overeat throughout the day. Instead, acknowledge that you've eaten more than you wanted on that one occasion, move on, and try to do better the rest of the day.

How to Use Your Workbook

Progress toward a goal! Obstacles! Success! Here's a place to keep track of it all. This workbook is meant to help you note your achievements, record your thoughts, and see what's working well (and maybe not quite so well) for you.

At the most basic level, this is a place for you to record your weight each week. If you want to leave it at that, fine. You've got a private spot to jot down the number the scale shows each week. Our hope is that you'll see the numbers moving in the right direction.

We've also provided space for you to write down your workouts, including the places you run and your thoughts on how running feels. If you want to, you can record your running and weight-loss goals.

The Food Log sections of the workbook will help you to think about serving sizes and the timing of your meals. As you're analyzing your eating habits and food choices, you might realize some things, things like "Hey, I always eat in front of my computer" or "A serving of granola is a lot smaller than a serving of Cheerios."

Readers willing to take the extra step and learn more about weight-loss math can use this workbook to go through some calculations. You don't need anything more than a calculator for simple addition, subtraction, and multiplication, so don't be intimidated if numbers aren't your strong suit.

You can calculate how many calories your body needs to maintain its current weight. You can count how many calories you're consuming and see how many calories walking and running will burn.

Not everyone wants to crunch the numbers, and we know that. But our experts also know that a little bit of information can be a powerful tool. Armed with knowledge about your own body and your own habits, you can develop a plan for training and weight loss that will work. Why? Because it's all yours.

THE FIRST WEIGH-IN

You should plan on weighing yourself every week and writing down the number. And there is a proper way to weigh. Try to weigh yourself on the same day of the week at the same time, ideally in the morning. Wake up, use the bathroom, take off your clothes, and step on the scale.

Take some measurements, too. Often when people get into shape, the scale doesn't do them justice. You can actually lose inches off your waist, hips, and thighs but not see the scale move much. That's because muscle weighs more than fat. Measurements give you another way to track progress.

So take a tape measure and measure your waist at the thinnest part. Pull the tape measure so it's snug against your body. Be sure to measure your chest, hips, thighs, and biceps at their widest parts. Although taking all these measurements can be beneficial for both sexes, guys are likely to notice the most change in their waist measurements and can just measure there if they prefer. However, ladies, I recommend you keep a close eye on your chest and hips as well.

Measure again at the end of each week, and you'll have a good record of all you've accomplished. Don't feel obligated to track all the measurements each week if you don't want to. If seeing no change in your biceps from week to week will discourage you, track your measurements every 6 weeks, or wait until the final weigh-in. Follow the system that works best for you.

HOW TO SET GOALS

We like goals that have a time frame and a number on them. That way, they're measurable. You can check back in on yourself at the end of the allotted time and say either "Yes, I've accomplished that goal" or "No, I'm halfway to my goal and I'll give myself another month."

The point is this: Give yourself specific goals and a target date for meeting them. Then you can see how you've done and know if it's time to set new ones. You'll be able to set goals on page 28.

STARTING STATS

Before you start the program, record your starting measurements below so that you'll be able to see changes in your body in real time when you compare your starting measurements to the progress you've made 12 weeks later! You can observe smaller-scale progress as the weeks pass by comparing the falling numbers on your weekly check-in pages. Seeing the numbers go in the right direction can help keep you motivated—and if the numbers aren't moving as much as you'd like, this info can cue you to modify the program to maximize your results.

HEIGHT __5' 1"__

WEIGHT __215.4__

BODY MASS INDEX (BMI)* __40.7__

CHEST __47"__

WAIST __43"__

HIPS (AT FULLEST PART) __53"__

LEFT THIGH __28"__

RIGHT THIGH __27.5"__

LEFT BICEPS __14"__

RIGHT BICEPS __14.5"__

*How to calculate your BMI: Multiply your weight in pounds by 703. Divide that number by your height in inches. Divide that number by your height in inches again.

GOAL SETTING

Take some time to think about your goals. They can be about running, racing, weight, health, even energy level. Consider: What do you really want for yourself? How do you envision yourself in the future? How hard are you willing to work to get there?

GOAL	DEADLINE FOR MEETING IT	HOW WILL YOU KNOW WHEN IT'S ACHIEVED?
Improved mood	ongoing	Things won't bother me as much; I'll have a buffer; I'll feel down less often.
Stomach gone	Dec. 31 2018	This hanging stomach will deflate, and I'll be left with a round but flatter stomach with no hang.
Smaller butt	Dec. 31 2018	
Hit 190 lbs.	Dec. 31 2018	I'll get on the scale and it'll say 190."
Hit 175 lbs.	March 31 2019	175."
Run a 5K	March 31 2019	Run the entire time, no walking.

Stage 1

WORKOUT SUMMARY

● **Walk for 30 minutes.**

Total workout time: 30 MINUTES

Do this workout at least three or four times in a week
before moving on to the next stage.

**BUDD'S
BUZZ**

"I've seen people start with a 3- or 4-minute walk,
depending on what their past is. The first day or two,
for example, they walk to the corner and then walk
back. Done. The third workout, maybe they build up to
7 minutes: up to the corner, turn left, then retrace their
steps home. Each day they keep walking a little farther.
The key is to be able to walk for 30 minutes before you
contemplate starting a running program."

DATE: 10·6·18

TIME WALKING: 30 mins

TOTAL WORKOUT TIME: 30 mins (156 calories)

COURSE: Irish Hill + Breslin Park (slight incline)

RATE HOW YOU FELT (1 being the worst and 10 being the best):

1   2   3   4   5   ⑥   7   8   9   10

OTHER PHYSICAL ACTIVITY:

NOTES (weather, injuries, etc.): Hot and humid, over 80.

FOOD LOG
STAGE 1 : DAY 1

2,034 - 156 = 1,878 (145 cal. def)

BREAKFAST: TIME 1 p.m.   ⊘ HUNGRY ○ NOT HUNGRY

Biscuit and gravy, yogurt parfait, coffee
w/ cream and splenda

TOTAL CALORIES OR SERVINGS 400 + 200 + 50 = 650

MIDMORNING SNACK: TIME_____   ○ HUNGRY ○ NOT HUNGRY

TOTAL CALORIES OR SERVINGS _____

LUNCH: TIME_____   ○ HUNGRY ○ NOT HUNGRY

TOTAL CALORIES OR SERVINGS _____

MIDAFTERNOON SNACK: TIME_____   ○ HUNGRY ○ NOT HUNGRY

TOTAL CALORIES OR SERVINGS _____

DINNER: TIME 5³⁰   ○ HUNGRY ⊘ NOT HUNGRY

Pigs in blanket: 6 mini crab cakes: 6 1 glass white
wine, 1 glass prosecco, 10 tortilla chips, 2 tbsp dip, 1 pc cake

TOTAL CALORIES OR SERVINGS 250 + 220 + 140 + 124 + 150 + 100 + 400 = 1,384

NIGHTTIME SNACK: TIME_____   ○ HUNGRY ○ NOT HUNGRY

TOTAL CALORIES OR SERVINGS _____

Run
Your
Butt
Off!

WORKOUT
STAGE 1 : DAY 2

DATE: _10·7·18_

TIME WALKING: _30 min_

TOTAL WORKOUT TIME: _30 min_

COURSE: _Irish Hill, Breslin Park, high 70's_
low 80s , 150 calories

RATE HOW YOU FELT (1 being the worst and 10 being the best):

1   2   3   4   5   ⑥   7   8   9   10

OTHER PHYSICAL ACTIVITY: _____

NOTES (weather, injuries, etc.): _I feel exhausted. My_
feet hurt. Blister from Harry Potter World.
Muscle in instep hurts. No energy. I
would not survive the zombie apocalypse.

FOOD LOG
STAGE 1 : DAY 2

BREAKFAST: TIME _11 30 AM_   ☑ HUNGRY   ○ NOT HUNGRY

Leftover biscuit and sausage gravy

TOTAL CALORIES OR SERVINGS _400 cal_

MIDMORNING SNACK: TIME_____   ○ HUNGRY   ○ NOT HUNGRY

TOTAL CALORIES OR SERVINGS _____

LUNCH: TIME _1 30_   ○ HUNGRY   ○ NOT HUNGRY

Skim milk and 2 Nature Valley granola bars.

TOTAL CALORIES OR SERVINGS _180 + 190 = 370_

MIDAFTERNOON SNACK: TIME _2 30_   ○ HUNGRY   ☑ NOT HUNGRY

La Colombe Vanilla

TOTAL CALORIES OR SERVINGS _140_

DINNER: TIME _8 pm_   ☑ HUNGRY   ○ NOT HUNGRY

Sausage and pharaoh, 16 oz dark beer, 2 Oreos

TOTAL CALORIES OR SERVINGS _350 + 250 + 140 = 740_

NIGHTTIME SNACK: TIME _10 40_   ☑ HUNGRY   ○ NOT HUNGRY

granola bars.

TOTAL CALORIES OR SERVINGS _190_

_1,810 - 150 = 1,660 =_
~ 400 cal def.

WORKOUT
STAGE 1 : DAY 3

DATE: _____

TIME WALKING: _____

TOTAL WORKOUT TIME: _____

COURSE: _____

_____

RATE HOW YOU FELT (1 being the worst and 10 being the best):

1   2   3   4   5   6   7   8   9   10

OTHER PHYSICAL ACTIVITY: _____

_____

NOTES (weather, injuries, etc.): _____

_____

_____

_____

_____

_____

_____

_____

_____

FOOD LOG
STAGE 1 : DAY 3

BREAKFAST: TIME _8AM_ ☑ HUNGRY ○ NOT HUNGRY

Nature valley granola, skimmilk

TOTAL CALORIES OR SERVINGS _380 + 180 = 560_

MIDMORNING SNACK: TIME_____ ○ HUNGRY ○ NOT HUNGRY

TOTAL CALORIES OR SERVINGS _____

LUNCH: TIME_____ ○ HUNGRY ○ NOT HUNGRY

TOTAL CALORIES OR SERVINGS _____

MIDAFTERNOON SNACK: TIME_____ ○ HUNGRY ○ NOT HUNGRY

TOTAL CALORIES OR SERVINGS _____

DINNER: TIME_____ ○ HUNGRY ○ NOT HUNGRY

TOTAL CALORIES OR SERVINGS _____

NIGHTTIME SNACK: TIME_____ ○ HUNGRY ○ NOT HUNGRY

TOTAL CALORIES OR SERVINGS _____

WORKOUT
STAGE 1 : DAY 4

DATE: _____

TIME WALKING: _____

TOTAL WORKOUT TIME: _____

COURSE: _____

_____

RATE HOW YOU FELT (1 being the worst and 10 being the best):

1   2   3   4   5   6   7   8   9   10

OTHER PHYSICAL ACTIVITY: _____

_____

NOTES (weather, injuries, etc.): _____

_____

_____

_____

_____

_____

_____

_____

FOOD LOG
STAGE 1 : DAY 4

BREAKFAST: TIME_____   ○ HUNGRY   ○ NOT HUNGRY

_____

_____

TOTAL CALORIES OR SERVINGS _____

MIDMORNING SNACK: TIME_____   ○ HUNGRY   ○ NOT HUNGRY

_____

TOTAL CALORIES OR SERVINGS _____

LUNCH: TIME_____   ○ HUNGRY   ○ NOT HUNGRY

_____

_____

TOTAL CALORIES OR SERVINGS _____

MIDAFTERNOON SNACK: TIME_____   ○ HUNGRY   ○ NOT HUNGRY

_____

TOTAL CALORIES OR SERVINGS _____

DINNER: TIME_____   ○ HUNGRY   ○ NOT HUNGRY

_____

_____

TOTAL CALORIES OR SERVINGS _____

NIGHTTIME SNACK: TIME_____   ○ HUNGRY   ○ NOT HUNGRY

_____

TOTAL CALORIES OR SERVINGS _____

WORKOUT
STAGE 1 : DAY 5

DATE: _____

TIME WALKING: _____

TOTAL WORKOUT TIME: _____

COURSE: _____

_____

RATE HOW YOU FELT (1 being the worst and 10 being the best):

1   2   3   4   5   6   7   8   9   10

OTHER PHYSICAL ACTIVITY: _____

_____

NOTES (weather, injuries, etc.): _____

_____

_____

_____

_____

_____

_____

_____

_____

FOOD LOG
STAGE 1 : DAY 5

BREAKFAST: TIME_____   ○ HUNGRY   ○ NOT HUNGRY

TOTAL CALORIES OR SERVINGS _____

MIDMORNING SNACK: TIME_____   ○ HUNGRY   ○ NOT HUNGRY

TOTAL CALORIES OR SERVINGS _____

LUNCH: TIME_____   ○ HUNGRY   ○ NOT HUNGRY

TOTAL CALORIES OR SERVINGS _____

MIDAFTERNOON SNACK: TIME_____   ○ HUNGRY   ○ NOT HUNGRY

TOTAL CALORIES OR SERVINGS _____

DINNER: TIME_____   ○ HUNGRY   ○ NOT HUNGRY

TOTAL CALORIES OR SERVINGS _____

NIGHTTIME SNACK: TIME_____   ○ HUNGRY   ○ NOT HUNGRY

TOTAL CALORIES OR SERVINGS _____

WORKOUT
STAGE 1 : DAY 6

DATE: _____

TIME WALKING: _____

TOTAL WORKOUT TIME: _____

COURSE: _____

_____

RATE HOW YOU FELT (1 being the worst and 10 being the best):

1   2   3   4   5   6   7   8   9   10

OTHER PHYSICAL ACTIVITY: _____

_____

NOTES (weather, injuries, etc.): _____

_____

_____

_____

_____

_____

_____

_____

_____

FOOD LOG
STAGE 1 : DAY 6

BREAKFAST: TIME_____   ○ HUNGRY   ○ NOT HUNGRY

_____

_____

TOTAL CALORIES OR SERVINGS _____

MIDMORNING SNACK: TIME_____   ○ HUNGRY   ○ NOT HUNGRY

_____

TOTAL CALORIES OR SERVINGS _____

LUNCH: TIME_____   ○ HUNGRY   ○ NOT HUNGRY

_____

_____

TOTAL CALORIES OR SERVINGS _____

MIDAFTERNOON SNACK: TIME_____   ○ HUNGRY   ○ NOT HUNGRY

_____

TOTAL CALORIES OR SERVINGS _____

DINNER: TIME_____   ○ HUNGRY   ○ NOT HUNGRY

_____

_____

TOTAL CALORIES OR SERVINGS _____

NIGHTTIME SNACK: TIME_____   ○ HUNGRY   ○ NOT HUNGRY

_____

TOTAL CALORIES OR SERVINGS _____

WORKOUT
STAGE 1 : DAY 7

DATE: _____

TIME WALKING: _____

TOTAL WORKOUT TIME: _____

COURSE: _____

_____

RATE HOW YOU FELT (1 being the worst and 10 being the best):

1   2   3   4   5   6   7   8   9   10

OTHER PHYSICAL ACTIVITY: _____

_____

NOTES (weather, injuries, etc.): _____

_____

_____

_____

_____

_____

_____

_____

_____

FOOD LOG
STAGE 1 : DAY 7

BREAKFAST: TIME_____   ○ HUNGRY   ○ NOT HUNGRY

_____

_____

TOTAL CALORIES OR SERVINGS _____

MIDMORNING SNACK: TIME_____   ○ HUNGRY   ○ NOT HUNGRY

_____

TOTAL CALORIES OR SERVINGS _____

LUNCH: TIME_____   ○ HUNGRY   ○ NOT HUNGRY

_____

_____

TOTAL CALORIES OR SERVINGS _____

MIDAFTERNOON SNACK: TIME_____   ○ HUNGRY   ○ NOT HUNGRY

_____

TOTAL CALORIES OR SERVINGS _____

DINNER: TIME_____   ○ HUNGRY   ○ NOT HUNGRY

_____

_____

TOTAL CALORIES OR SERVINGS _____

NIGHTTIME SNACK: TIME_____   ○ HUNGRY   ○ NOT HUNGRY

_____

TOTAL CALORIES OR SERVINGS _____

Stage 1 CHECK-IN

WEIGHT_____

CHEST_____

WAIST_____

HIPS (AT FULLEST PART)_____

LEFT THIGH_____

RIGHT THIGH_____

LEFT BICEPS_____

RIGHT BICEPS_____

THOUGHTS ON THE WORKOUTS: Record the weather, your effort level, aches and pains, challenges, and successes. How hard did it feel?

_____

_____

_____

GOALS UPDATE

GOAL	DEADLINE FOR MEETING IT	MET GOAL/STILL IN PROGRESS

Stage 2

WORKOUT SUMMARY

- Walk for 4 minutes. Run for 1 minute.
- Repeat that sequence four more times.
- End with 4 minutes of walking.

Total workout time:
29 MINUTES, 5 of which are running

Do this workout at least three or four times in a week
before moving on to the next stage.

BUDD'S BUZZ : "Try to keep your breathing under control. If you're looking at your watch and you're thinking, 'When will this minute be over?' you're going too fast."

DATE: _____

TIME WALKING: _____

TIME RUNNING: _____

TOTAL WORKOUT TIME: _____

COURSE: _____

_____

RATE HOW YOU FELT (1 being the worst and 10 being the best):

1   2   3   4   5   6   7   8   9   10

OTHER PHYSICAL ACTIVITY: _____

_____

NOTES (weather, injuries, etc.): _____

_____

_____

_____

_____

_____

_____

_____

FOOD LOG
STAGE 2 : DAY 1

BREAKFAST: TIME_____   ○ HUNGRY   ○ NOT HUNGRY

_____

_____

TOTAL CALORIES OR SERVINGS _____

MIDMORNING SNACK: TIME_____   ○ HUNGRY   ○ NOT HUNGRY

_____

TOTAL CALORIES OR SERVINGS _____

LUNCH: TIME_____   ○ HUNGRY   ○ NOT HUNGRY

_____

_____

TOTAL CALORIES OR SERVINGS _____

MIDAFTERNOON SNACK: TIME_____   ○ HUNGRY   ○ NOT HUNGRY

_____

TOTAL CALORIES OR SERVINGS _____

DINNER: TIME_____   ○ HUNGRY   ○ NOT HUNGRY

_____

_____

TOTAL CALORIES OR SERVINGS _____

NIGHTTIME SNACK: TIME_____   ○ HUNGRY   ○ NOT HUNGRY

_____

TOTAL CALORIES OR SERVINGS _____

DATE: _____

TIME WALKING: _____

TIME RUNNING: _____

TOTAL WORKOUT TIME: _____

COURSE: _____

_____

RATE HOW YOU FELT (1 being the worst and 10 being the best):

| 1 | 2 | 3 | 4 | 5 | 6 | 7 | 8 | 9 | 10 |

OTHER PHYSICAL ACTIVITY: _____

_____

NOTES (weather, injuries, etc.): _____

_____

_____

_____

_____

_____

_____

_____

FOOD LOG
STAGE 2 : DAY 2

BREAKFAST: TIME_____   ○ HUNGRY   ○ NOT HUNGRY

_____

_____

TOTAL CALORIES OR SERVINGS _____

MIDMORNING SNACK: TIME_____   ○ HUNGRY   ○ NOT HUNGRY

_____

TOTAL CALORIES OR SERVINGS _____

LUNCH: TIME_____   ○ HUNGRY   ○ NOT HUNGRY

_____

_____

TOTAL CALORIES OR SERVINGS _____

MIDAFTERNOON SNACK: TIME_____   ○ HUNGRY   ○ NOT HUNGRY

_____

TOTAL CALORIES OR SERVINGS _____

DINNER: TIME_____   ○ HUNGRY   ○ NOT HUNGRY

_____

_____

TOTAL CALORIES OR SERVINGS _____

NIGHTTIME SNACK: TIME_____   ○ HUNGRY   ○ NOT HUNGRY

_____

TOTAL CALORIES OR SERVINGS _____

WORKOUT
STAGE 2 : DAY 3

DATE: _____

TIME WALKING: _____

TIME RUNNING: _____

TOTAL WORKOUT TIME: _____

COURSE: _____

_____

RATE HOW YOU FELT (1 being the worst and 10 being the best):

1   2   3   4   5   6   7   8   9   10

OTHER PHYSICAL ACTIVITY: _____

_____

NOTES (weather, injuries, etc.): _____

_____

_____

_____

_____

_____

_____

_____

FOOD LOG
STAGE 2 : DAY 3

BREAKFAST: TIME_____   ○ HUNGRY   ○ NOT HUNGRY

_____

_____

TOTAL CALORIES OR SERVINGS _____

MIDMORNING SNACK: TIME_____   ○ HUNGRY   ○ NOT HUNGRY

_____

TOTAL CALORIES OR SERVINGS _____

LUNCH: TIME_____   ○ HUNGRY   ○ NOT HUNGRY

_____

_____

TOTAL CALORIES OR SERVINGS _____

MIDAFTERNOON SNACK: TIME_____   ○ HUNGRY   ○ NOT HUNGRY

_____

TOTAL CALORIES OR SERVINGS _____

DINNER: TIME_____   ○ HUNGRY   ○ NOT HUNGRY

_____

_____

TOTAL CALORIES OR SERVINGS _____

NIGHTTIME SNACK: TIME_____   ○ HUNGRY   ○ NOT HUNGRY

_____

TOTAL CALORIES OR SERVINGS _____

Run Your Butt Off!

WORKOUT
STAGE 2 : DAY 4

DATE: _____

TIME WALKING: _____

TIME RUNNING: _____

TOTAL WORKOUT TIME: _____

COURSE: _____

_____

RATE HOW YOU FELT (1 being the worst and 10 being the best):

1   2   3   4   5   6   7   8   9   10

OTHER PHYSICAL ACTIVITY: _____

_____

NOTES (weather, injuries, etc.): _____

_____

_____

_____

_____

_____

_____

_____

FOOD LOG
STAGE 2 : DAY 4

BREAKFAST: TIME_____   ○ HUNGRY   ○ NOT HUNGRY

_____

_____

_____

TOTAL CALORIES OR SERVINGS _____

MIDMORNING SNACK: TIME_____   ○ HUNGRY   ○ NOT HUNGRY

_____

TOTAL CALORIES OR SERVINGS _____

LUNCH: TIME_____   ○ HUNGRY   ○ NOT HUNGRY

_____

_____

_____

TOTAL CALORIES OR SERVINGS _____

MIDAFTERNOON SNACK: TIME_____   ○ HUNGRY   ○ NOT HUNGRY

_____

TOTAL CALORIES OR SERVINGS _____

DINNER: TIME_____   ○ HUNGRY   ○ NOT HUNGRY

_____

_____

TOTAL CALORIES OR SERVINGS _____

NIGHTTIME SNACK: TIME_____   ○ HUNGRY   ○ NOT HUNGRY

_____

TOTAL CALORIES OR SERVINGS _____

DATE: _____

TIME WALKING: _____

TIME RUNNING: _____

TOTAL WORKOUT TIME: _____

COURSE: _____

_____

RATE HOW YOU FELT (1 being the worst and 10 being the best):

| 1 | 2 | 3 | 4 | 5 | 6 | 7 | 8 | 9 | 10 |

OTHER PHYSICAL ACTIVITY: _____

_____

NOTES (weather, injuries, etc.): _____

_____

_____

_____

_____

_____

_____

_____

FOOD LOG
STAGE 2 : DAY 5

BREAKFAST: TIME_____   ○ HUNGRY   ○ NOT HUNGRY

_____

_____

TOTAL CALORIES OR SERVINGS _____

MIDMORNING SNACK: TIME_____   ○ HUNGRY   ○ NOT HUNGRY

_____

TOTAL CALORIES OR SERVINGS _____

LUNCH: TIME_____   ○ HUNGRY   ○ NOT HUNGRY

_____

_____

TOTAL CALORIES OR SERVINGS _____

MIDAFTERNOON SNACK: TIME_____   ○ HUNGRY   ○ NOT HUNGRY

_____

TOTAL CALORIES OR SERVINGS _____

DINNER: TIME_____   ○ HUNGRY   ○ NOT HUNGRY

_____

_____

TOTAL CALORIES OR SERVINGS _____

NIGHTTIME SNACK: TIME_____   ○ HUNGRY   ○ NOT HUNGRY

_____

TOTAL CALORIES OR SERVINGS _____

WORKOUT
STAGE 2 : DAY 6

DATE: _____

TIME WALKING: _____

TIME RUNNING: _____

TOTAL WORKOUT TIME: _____

COURSE: _____

_____

RATE HOW YOU FELT (1 being the worst and 10 being the best):

1   2   3   4   5   6   7   8   9   10

OTHER PHYSICAL ACTIVITY: _____

_____

NOTES (weather, injuries, etc.): _____

_____

_____

_____

_____

_____

_____

_____

FOOD LOG
STAGE 2 : DAY 6

BREAKFAST: TIME_____   ○ HUNGRY   ○ NOT HUNGRY

_____

_____

TOTAL CALORIES OR SERVINGS _____

MIDMORNING SNACK: TIME_____   ○ HUNGRY   ○ NOT HUNGRY

_____

TOTAL CALORIES OR SERVINGS _____

LUNCH: TIME_____   ○ HUNGRY   ○ NOT HUNGRY

_____

_____

TOTAL CALORIES OR SERVINGS _____

MIDAFTERNOON SNACK: TIME_____   ○ HUNGRY   ○ NOT HUNGRY

_____

TOTAL CALORIES OR SERVINGS _____

DINNER: TIME_____   ○ HUNGRY   ○ NOT HUNGRY

_____

_____

TOTAL CALORIES OR SERVINGS _____

NIGHTTIME SNACK: TIME_____   ○ HUNGRY   ○ NOT HUNGRY

_____

TOTAL CALORIES OR SERVINGS _____

WORKOUT
STAGE 2 : DAY 7

DATE: _____

TIME WALKING: _____

TIME RUNNING: _____

TOTAL WORKOUT TIME: _____

COURSE: _____

_____

RATE HOW YOU FELT (1 being the worst and 10 being the best):

1   2   3   4   5   6   7   8   9   10

OTHER PHYSICAL ACTIVITY: _____

_____

NOTES (weather, injuries, etc.): _____

_____

_____

_____

_____

_____

_____

_____

FOOD LOG
STAGE 2 : DAY 7

BREAKFAST: TIME_____   ○ HUNGRY   ○ NOT HUNGRY

_____

_____

TOTAL CALORIES OR SERVINGS _____

MIDMORNING SNACK: TIME_____   ○ HUNGRY   ○ NOT HUNGRY

_____

TOTAL CALORIES OR SERVINGS _____

LUNCH: TIME_____   ○ HUNGRY   ○ NOT HUNGRY

_____

_____

TOTAL CALORIES OR SERVINGS _____

MIDAFTERNOON SNACK: TIME_____   ○ HUNGRY   ○ NOT HUNGRY

_____

TOTAL CALORIES OR SERVINGS _____

DINNER: TIME_____   ○ HUNGRY   ○ NOT HUNGRY

_____

_____

TOTAL CALORIES OR SERVINGS _____

NIGHTTIME SNACK: TIME_____   ○ HUNGRY   ○ NOT HUNGRY

_____

TOTAL CALORIES OR SERVINGS _____

Stage 2 CHECK-IN

WEIGHT_____

CHEST_____

WAIST_____

HIPS (AT FULLEST PART)_____

LEFT THIGH_____

RIGHT THIGH_____

LEFT BICEPS_____

RIGHT BICEPS_____

THOUGHTS ON THE WORKOUTS: Record the weather, your effort level, aches and pains, challenges, and successes. How hard did it feel?

_____

_____

_____

GOALS UPDATE

GOAL	DEADLINE FOR MEETING IT	MET GOAL/STILL IN PROGRESS

Stage 3

WORKOUT SUMMARY

 Walk for 4 minutes. Run for 2 minutes.

Repeat that sequence four more times.

End with 3 minutes of walking.

Total workout time:
33 MINUTES, 10 of which are running

Do this workout at least three or four times in a week before moving on to the next stage.

BUDD'S BUZZ "The point is consistency. Don't step it up until you get a solid week in at one level. I usually tell people to step back a week from their last training session if they've been sick. If they moved from 1 minute of running and 4 of walking to 2 minutes of running and 4 of walking, they should go back to 1 minute of running. If that's too easy after their first session back, they can resume running 2, walking 4."

DATE: _____

TIME WALKING: _____

TIME RUNNING: _____

TOTAL WORKOUT TIME: _____

COURSE: _____

_____

RATE HOW YOU FELT (1 being the worst and 10 being the best):

1   2   3   4   5   6   7   8   9   10

OTHER PHYSICAL ACTIVITY: _____

_____

NOTES (weather, injuries, etc.): _____

_____

_____

_____

_____

_____

_____

_____

FOOD LOG
STAGE 3 : DAY 1

BREAKFAST: TIME_____   ○ HUNGRY   ○ NOT HUNGRY

_____

_____

TOTAL CALORIES OR SERVINGS _____

MIDMORNING SNACK: TIME_____   ○ HUNGRY   ○ NOT HUNGRY

_____

TOTAL CALORIES OR SERVINGS _____

LUNCH: TIME_____   ○ HUNGRY   ○ NOT HUNGRY

_____

_____

TOTAL CALORIES OR SERVINGS _____

MIDAFTERNOON SNACK: TIME_____   ○ HUNGRY   ○ NOT HUNGRY

_____

TOTAL CALORIES OR SERVINGS _____

DINNER: TIME_____   ○ HUNGRY   ○ NOT HUNGRY

_____

_____

TOTAL CALORIES OR SERVINGS _____

NIGHTTIME SNACK: TIME_____   ○ HUNGRY   ○ NOT HUNGRY

_____

TOTAL CALORIES OR SERVINGS _____

WORKOUT
STAGE 3 : DAY 2

DATE: _____

TIME WALKING: _____

TIME RUNNING: _____

TOTAL WORKOUT TIME: _____

COURSE: _____

_____

RATE HOW YOU FELT (1 being the worst and 10 being the best):

1   2   3   4   5   6   7   8   9   10

OTHER PHYSICAL ACTIVITY: _____

_____

NOTES (weather, injuries, etc.): _____

_____

_____

_____

_____

_____

_____

_____

FOOD LOG
STAGE 3 : DAY 2

BREAKFAST: TIME_____   ○ HUNGRY ○ NOT HUNGRY

_____

_____

TOTAL CALORIES OR SERVINGS _____

MIDMORNING SNACK: TIME_____   ○ HUNGRY ○ NOT HUNGRY

_____

TOTAL CALORIES OR SERVINGS _____

LUNCH: TIME_____   ○ HUNGRY ○ NOT HUNGRY

_____

_____

TOTAL CALORIES OR SERVINGS _____

MIDAFTERNOON SNACK: TIME_____   ○ HUNGRY ○ NOT HUNGRY

_____

TOTAL CALORIES OR SERVINGS _____

DINNER: TIME_____   ○ HUNGRY ○ NOT HUNGRY

_____

_____

TOTAL CALORIES OR SERVINGS _____

NIGHTTIME SNACK: TIME_____   ○ HUNGRY ○ NOT HUNGRY

_____

TOTAL CALORIES OR SERVINGS _____

Run Your Butt Off!

WORKOUT
STAGE 3 : DAY 3

DATE: _____

TIME WALKING: _____

TIME RUNNING: _____

TOTAL WORKOUT TIME: _____

COURSE: _____

_____

RATE HOW YOU FELT (1 being the worst and 10 being the best):

1   2   3   4   5   6   7   8   9   10

OTHER PHYSICAL ACTIVITY: _____

_____

NOTES (weather, injuries, etc.): _____

_____

_____

_____

_____

_____

_____

_____

FOOD LOG
STAGE 3 : DAY 3

BREAKFAST: TIME_____   ○ HUNGRY   ○ NOT HUNGRY

_____

_____

TOTAL CALORIES OR SERVINGS _____

MIDMORNING SNACK: TIME_____   ○ HUNGRY   ○ NOT HUNGRY

_____

TOTAL CALORIES OR SERVINGS _____

LUNCH: TIME_____   ○ HUNGRY   ○ NOT HUNGRY

_____

_____

TOTAL CALORIES OR SERVINGS _____

MIDAFTERNOON SNACK: TIME_____   ○ HUNGRY   ○ NOT HUNGRY

_____

TOTAL CALORIES OR SERVINGS _____

DINNER: TIME_____   ○ HUNGRY   ○ NOT HUNGRY

_____

_____

TOTAL CALORIES OR SERVINGS _____

NIGHTTIME SNACK: TIME_____   ○ HUNGRY   ○ NOT HUNGRY

_____

TOTAL CALORIES OR SERVINGS _____

DATE: _____

TIME WALKING: _____

TIME RUNNING: _____

TOTAL WORKOUT TIME: _____

COURSE: _____

_____

RATE HOW YOU FELT (I being the worst and 10 being the best):

| I | 2 | 3 | 4 | 5 | 6 | 7 | 8 | 9 | 10 |

OTHER PHYSICAL ACTIVITY: _____

_____

NOTES (weather, injuries, etc.): _____

_____

_____

_____

_____

_____

_____

_____

FOOD LOG
STAGE 3 : DAY 4

BREAKFAST: TIME_____   ○ HUNGRY   ○ NOT HUNGRY

_____

_____

TOTAL CALORIES OR SERVINGS _____

MIDMORNING SNACK: TIME_____   ○ HUNGRY   ○ NOT HUNGRY

_____

TOTAL CALORIES OR SERVINGS _____

LUNCH: TIME_____   ○ HUNGRY   ○ NOT HUNGRY

_____

_____

TOTAL CALORIES OR SERVINGS _____

MIDAFTERNOON SNACK: TIME_____   ○ HUNGRY   ○ NOT HUNGRY

_____

TOTAL CALORIES OR SERVINGS _____

DINNER: TIME_____   ○ HUNGRY   ○ NOT HUNGRY

_____

_____

TOTAL CALORIES OR SERVINGS _____

NIGHTTIME SNACK: TIME_____   ○ HUNGRY   ○ NOT HUNGRY

_____

TOTAL CALORIES OR SERVINGS _____

DATE: _____

TIME WALKING: _____

TIME RUNNING: _____

TOTAL WORKOUT TIME: _____

COURSE: _____

_____

RATE HOW YOU FELT (1 being the worst and 10 being the best):

1   2   3   4   5   6   7   8   9   10

OTHER PHYSICAL ACTIVITY: _____

_____

NOTES (weather, injuries, etc.): _____

_____

_____

_____

_____

_____

_____

_____

_____

FOOD LOG
STAGE 3 : DAY 5

BREAKFAST: TIME_____   ○ HUNGRY   ○ NOT HUNGRY

_____

_____

TOTAL CALORIES OR SERVINGS _____

MIDMORNING SNACK: TIME_____   ○ HUNGRY   ○ NOT HUNGRY

_____

TOTAL CALORIES OR SERVINGS _____

LUNCH: TIME_____   ○ HUNGRY   ○ NOT HUNGRY

_____

_____

TOTAL CALORIES OR SERVINGS _____

MIDAFTERNOON SNACK: TIME_____   ○ HUNGRY   ○ NOT HUNGRY

_____

TOTAL CALORIES OR SERVINGS _____

DINNER: TIME_____   ○ HUNGRY   ○ NOT HUNGRY

_____

_____

TOTAL CALORIES OR SERVINGS _____

NIGHTTIME SNACK: TIME_____   ○ HUNGRY   ○ NOT HUNGRY

_____

TOTAL CALORIES OR SERVINGS _____

DATE: _____

TIME WALKING: _____

TIME RUNNING: _____

TOTAL WORKOUT TIME: _____

COURSE: _____

_____

RATE HOW YOU FELT (1 being the worst and 10 being the best):

1   2   3   4   5   6   7   8   9   10

OTHER PHYSICAL ACTIVITY: _____

_____

NOTES (weather, injuries, etc.): _____

_____

_____

_____

_____

_____

_____

_____

FOOD LOG
STAGE 3 : DAY 6

BREAKFAST: TIME_____   ○ HUNGRY   ○ NOT HUNGRY

_____

_____

TOTAL CALORIES OR SERVINGS _____

MIDMORNING SNACK: TIME_____   ○ HUNGRY   ○ NOT HUNGRY

_____

TOTAL CALORIES OR SERVINGS _____

LUNCH: TIME_____   ○ HUNGRY   ○ NOT HUNGRY

_____

_____

TOTAL CALORIES OR SERVINGS _____

MIDAFTERNOON SNACK: TIME_____   ○ HUNGRY   ○ NOT HUNGRY

_____

TOTAL CALORIES OR SERVINGS _____

DINNER: TIME_____   ○ HUNGRY   ○ NOT HUNGRY

_____

_____

TOTAL CALORIES OR SERVINGS _____

NIGHTTIME SNACK: TIME_____   ○ HUNGRY   ○ NOT HUNGRY

_____

TOTAL CALORIES OR SERVINGS _____

DATE: _____

TIME WALKING: _____

TIME RUNNING: _____

TOTAL WORKOUT TIME: _____

COURSE: _____

_____

RATE HOW YOU FELT (1 being the worst and 10 being the best):

1   2   3   4   5   6   7   8   9   10

OTHER PHYSICAL ACTIVITY: _____

_____

NOTES (weather, injuries, etc.): _____

_____

_____

_____

_____

_____

_____

_____

FOOD LOG
STAGE 3 : DAY 7

BREAKFAST: TIME_____ ○ HUNGRY ○ NOT HUNGRY

_____

_____

TOTAL CALORIES OR SERVINGS _____

MIDMORNING SNACK: TIME_____ ○ HUNGRY ○ NOT HUNGRY

_____

TOTAL CALORIES OR SERVINGS _____

LUNCH: TIME_____ ○ HUNGRY ○ NOT HUNGRY

_____

_____

TOTAL CALORIES OR SERVINGS _____

MIDAFTERNOON SNACK: TIME_____ ○ HUNGRY ○ NOT HUNGRY

_____

TOTAL CALORIES OR SERVINGS _____

DINNER: TIME_____ ○ HUNGRY ○ NOT HUNGRY

_____

_____

TOTAL CALORIES OR SERVINGS _____

NIGHTTIME SNACK: TIME_____ ○ HUNGRY ○ NOT HUNGRY

_____

TOTAL CALORIES OR SERVINGS _____

Stage 3 CHECK-IN

WEIGHT_____

CHEST_____

WAIST_____

HIPS (AT FULLEST PART)_____

LEFT THIGH_____

RIGHT THIGH_____

LEFT BICEPS_____

RIGHT BICEPS_____

THOUGHTS ON THE WORKOUTS: Record the weather, your effort level, aches and pains, challenges, and successes. How hard did it feel?

_____

_____

_____

GOALS UPDATE

GOAL	DEADLINE FOR MEETING IT	MET GOAL/STILL IN PROGRESS

Stage 4

WORKOUT SUMMARY

- Walk for 3 minutes. Run for 3 minutes.
- Repeat that sequence four more times.
- End with 3 minutes of walking.

**Total workout time:
33 MINUTES, 15 of which are running**

Do this workout at least three or four times in a week
before moving on to the next stage.

**BUDD'S
BUZZ**
"You don't want to pay a whole lot of attention to how
fast you're going on a treadmill. Use your own sense of
effort to guide your speed. Put a towel over the console.
When you want to speed up, stick your finger on the
button under the towel and increase the speed to the
point where you feel comfortable running. Don't look at
the number. Don't get sucked in at a pace the preset
program on the treadmill tells you to go or a pace you
think you should be going."

WORKOUT
STAGE 4 : DAY 1

DATE: _____

TIME WALKING: _____

TIME RUNNING: _____

TOTAL WORKOUT TIME: _____

COURSE: _____

_____

RATE HOW YOU FELT (1 being the worst and 10 being the best):

1   2   3   4   5   6   7   8   9   10

OTHER PHYSICAL ACTIVITY: _____

_____

NOTES (weather, injuries, etc.): _____

_____

_____

_____

_____

_____

_____

_____

FOOD LOG
STAGE 4 : DAY 1

BREAKFAST: TIME_____   ○ HUNGRY   ○ NOT HUNGRY

_____

_____

TOTAL CALORIES OR SERVINGS _____

MIDMORNING SNACK: TIME_____   ○ HUNGRY   ○ NOT HUNGRY

_____

TOTAL CALORIES OR SERVINGS _____

LUNCH: TIME_____   ○ HUNGRY   ○ NOT HUNGRY

_____

_____

TOTAL CALORIES OR SERVINGS _____

MIDAFTERNOON SNACK: TIME_____   ○ HUNGRY   ○ NOT HUNGRY

_____

TOTAL CALORIES OR SERVINGS _____

DINNER: TIME_____   ○ HUNGRY   ○ NOT HUNGRY

_____

_____

TOTAL CALORIES OR SERVINGS _____

NIGHTTIME SNACK: TIME_____   ○ HUNGRY   ○ NOT HUNGRY

_____

TOTAL CALORIES OR SERVINGS _____

DATE: _____

TIME WALKING: _____

TIME RUNNING: _____

TOTAL WORKOUT TIME: _____

COURSE: _____

_____

RATE HOW YOU FELT (1 being the worst and 10 being the best):

1   2   3   4   5   6   7   8   9   10

OTHER PHYSICAL ACTIVITY: _____

_____

NOTES (weather, injuries, etc.): _____

_____

_____

_____

_____

_____

_____

_____

FOOD LOG
STAGE 4 : DAY 2

BREAKFAST: TIME_____   ○ HUNGRY   ○ NOT HUNGRY

_____

_____

TOTAL CALORIES OR SERVINGS _____

MIDMORNING SNACK: TIME_____   ○ HUNGRY   ○ NOT HUNGRY

_____

TOTAL CALORIES OR SERVINGS _____

LUNCH: TIME_____   ○ HUNGRY   ○ NOT HUNGRY

_____

_____

TOTAL CALORIES OR SERVINGS _____

MIDAFTERNOON SNACK: TIME_____   ○ HUNGRY   ○ NOT HUNGRY

_____

TOTAL CALORIES OR SERVINGS _____

DINNER: TIME_____   ○ HUNGRY   ○ NOT HUNGRY

_____

_____

TOTAL CALORIES OR SERVINGS _____

NIGHTTIME SNACK: TIME_____   ○ HUNGRY   ○ NOT HUNGRY

_____

TOTAL CALORIES OR SERVINGS _____

DATE: _____

TIME WALKING: _____

TIME RUNNING: _____

TOTAL WORKOUT TIME: _____

COURSE: _____

_____

RATE HOW YOU FELT (1 being the worst and 10 being the best):

1   2   3   4   5   6   7   8   9   10

OTHER PHYSICAL ACTIVITY: _____

_____

NOTES (weather, injuries, etc.): _____

_____

_____

_____

_____

_____

_____

_____

FOOD LOG
STAGE 4 : DAY 3

BREAKFAST: TIME_____   ○ HUNGRY   ○ NOT HUNGRY

_____

_____

TOTAL CALORIES OR SERVINGS _____

MIDMORNING SNACK: TIME_____   ○ HUNGRY   ○ NOT HUNGRY

_____

TOTAL CALORIES OR SERVINGS _____

LUNCH: TIME_____   ○ HUNGRY   ○ NOT HUNGRY

_____

_____

TOTAL CALORIES OR SERVINGS _____

MIDAFTERNOON SNACK: TIME_____   ○ HUNGRY   ○ NOT HUNGRY

_____

TOTAL CALORIES OR SERVINGS _____

DINNER: TIME_____   ○ HUNGRY   ○ NOT HUNGRY

_____

_____

TOTAL CALORIES OR SERVINGS _____

NIGHTTIME SNACK: TIME_____   ○ HUNGRY   ○ NOT HUNGRY

_____

TOTAL CALORIES OR SERVINGS _____

Run Your Butt Off!

WORKOUT
STAGE 4 : DAY 4

DATE: _____

TIME WALKING: _____

TIME RUNNING: _____

TOTAL WORKOUT TIME: _____

COURSE: _____

_____

RATE HOW YOU FELT (1 being the worst and 10 being the best):

1   2   3   4   5   6   7   8   9   10

OTHER PHYSICAL ACTIVITY: _____

_____

NOTES (weather, injuries, etc.): _____

_____

_____

_____

_____

_____

_____

FOOD LOG
STAGE 4 : DAY 4

BREAKFAST: TIME_____   ○ HUNGRY   ○ NOT HUNGRY

_____

_____

TOTAL CALORIES OR SERVINGS _____

MIDMORNING SNACK: TIME_____   ○ HUNGRY   ○ NOT HUNGRY

_____

TOTAL CALORIES OR SERVINGS _____

LUNCH: TIME_____   ○ HUNGRY   ○ NOT HUNGRY

_____

_____

TOTAL CALORIES OR SERVINGS _____

MIDAFTERNOON SNACK: TIME_____   ○ HUNGRY   ○ NOT HUNGRY

_____

TOTAL CALORIES OR SERVINGS _____

DINNER: TIME_____   ○ HUNGRY   ○ NOT HUNGRY

_____

_____

TOTAL CALORIES OR SERVINGS _____

NIGHTTIME SNACK: TIME_____   ○ HUNGRY   ○ NOT HUNGRY

_____

TOTAL CALORIES OR SERVINGS _____

DATE: _____

TIME WALKING: _____

TIME RUNNING: _____

TOTAL WORKOUT TIME: _____

COURSE: _____
_____

RATE HOW YOU FELT (1 being the worst and 10 being the best):

1   2   3   4   5   6   7   8   9   10

OTHER PHYSICAL ACTIVITY: _____
_____

NOTES (weather, injuries, etc.): _____
_____
_____
_____
_____
_____
_____
_____

FOOD LOG
STAGE 4 : DAY 5

BREAKFAST: TIME_____   ○ HUNGRY   ○ NOT HUNGRY

_____

_____

TOTAL CALORIES OR SERVINGS _____

MIDMORNING SNACK: TIME_____   ○ HUNGRY   ○ NOT HUNGRY

_____

TOTAL CALORIES OR SERVINGS _____

LUNCH: TIME_____   ○ HUNGRY   ○ NOT HUNGRY

_____

_____

TOTAL CALORIES OR SERVINGS _____

MIDAFTERNOON SNACK: TIME_____   ○ HUNGRY   ○ NOT HUNGRY

_____

TOTAL CALORIES OR SERVINGS _____

DINNER: TIME_____   ○ HUNGRY   ○ NOT HUNGRY

_____

_____

TOTAL CALORIES OR SERVINGS _____

NIGHTTIME SNACK: TIME_____   ○ HUNGRY   ○ NOT HUNGRY

_____

TOTAL CALORIES OR SERVINGS _____

Run Your Butt Off!

WORKOUT
STAGE 4 : DAY 6

DATE: _____

TIME WALKING: _____

TIME RUNNING: _____

TOTAL WORKOUT TIME: _____

COURSE: _____

_____

RATE HOW YOU FELT (1 being the worst and 10 being the best):

1   2   3   4   5   6   7   8   9   10

OTHER PHYSICAL ACTIVITY: _____

_____

NOTES (weather, injuries, etc.): _____

_____

_____

_____

_____

_____

_____

FOOD LOG
STAGE 4 : DAY 6

BREAKFAST: TIME_____   ○ HUNGRY   ○ NOT HUNGRY

_____

_____

TOTAL CALORIES OR SERVINGS _____

MIDMORNING SNACK: TIME_____   ○ HUNGRY   ○ NOT HUNGRY

_____

TOTAL CALORIES OR SERVINGS _____

LUNCH: TIME_____   ○ HUNGRY   ○ NOT HUNGRY

_____

_____

TOTAL CALORIES OR SERVINGS _____

MIDAFTERNOON SNACK: TIME_____   ○ HUNGRY   ○ NOT HUNGRY

_____

TOTAL CALORIES OR SERVINGS _____

DINNER: TIME_____   ○ HUNGRY   ○ NOT HUNGRY

_____

_____

TOTAL CALORIES OR SERVINGS _____

NIGHTTIME SNACK: TIME_____   ○ HUNGRY   ○ NOT HUNGRY

_____

TOTAL CALORIES OR SERVINGS _____

DATE: _____

TIME WALKING: _____

TIME RUNNING: _____

TOTAL WORKOUT TIME: _____

COURSE: _____
_____

RATE HOW YOU FELT (1 being the worst and 10 being the best):

| 1 | 2 | 3 | 4 | 5 | 6 | 7 | 8 | 9 | 10 |

OTHER PHYSICAL ACTIVITY: _____
_____

NOTES (weather, injuries, etc.): _____
_____
_____
_____
_____
_____
_____
_____

FOOD LOG
STAGE 4 : DAY 7

BREAKFAST: TIME_____   ○ HUNGRY   ○ NOT HUNGRY

_____

_____

TOTAL CALORIES OR SERVINGS _____

MIDMORNING SNACK: TIME_____   ○ HUNGRY   ○ NOT HUNGRY

_____

TOTAL CALORIES OR SERVINGS _____

LUNCH: TIME_____   ○ HUNGRY   ○ NOT HUNGRY

_____

_____

TOTAL CALORIES OR SERVINGS _____

MIDAFTERNOON SNACK: TIME_____   ○ HUNGRY   ○ NOT HUNGRY

_____

TOTAL CALORIES OR SERVINGS _____

DINNER: TIME_____   ○ HUNGRY   ○ NOT HUNGRY

_____

_____

TOTAL CALORIES OR SERVINGS _____

NIGHTTIME SNACK: TIME_____   ○ HUNGRY   ○ NOT HUNGRY

_____

TOTAL CALORIES OR SERVINGS _____

Stage 4 CHECK-IN

WEIGHT_____

CHEST_____

WAIST_____

HIPS (AT FULLEST PART)_____

LEFT THIGH_____

RIGHT THIGH_____

LEFT BICEPS_____

RIGHT BICEPS_____

THOUGHTS ON THE WORKOUTS: Record the weather, your effort level, aches and pains, challenges, and successes. How hard did it feel?

_____

_____

_____

GOALS UPDATE

GOAL	DEADLINE FOR MEETING IT	MET GOAL/STILL IN PROGRESS

Stage 5

WORKOUT SUMMARY

- Walk for 2 minutes 30 seconds. Run for 5 minutes.
- Repeat that sequence three more times.
- End with 3 minutes of walking.

**Total workout time:
33 MINUTES, 20 of which are running**

Do this workout at least three or four times in a week before moving on to the next stage.

BUDD'S BUZZ

"The biggest thing is looking long term. Develop consistency in your new lifestyle. The mistake people make is that they try to do a whole lot all at once, and then they take a period of time off. Then they do that again: a whole lot at once, followed by a long time off. When you're putting together the schedule, ask yourself, 'Can I do this over and over?'"

WORKOUT
STAGE 5 : DAY 1

DATE: _____

TIME WALKING: _____

TIME RUNNING: _____

TOTAL WORKOUT TIME: _____

COURSE: _____

_____

RATE HOW YOU FELT (1 being the worst and 10 being the best):

1   2   3   4   5   6   7   8   9   10

OTHER PHYSICAL ACTIVITY: _____

_____

NOTES (weather, injuries, etc.): _____

_____

_____

_____

_____

_____

_____

_____

FOOD LOG
STAGE 5 : DAY 1

BREAKFAST: TIME_____   ○ HUNGRY   ○ NOT HUNGRY

_____

_____

TOTAL CALORIES OR SERVINGS _____

MIDMORNING SNACK: TIME_____   ○ HUNGRY   ○ NOT HUNGRY

_____

TOTAL CALORIES OR SERVINGS _____

LUNCH: TIME_____   ○ HUNGRY   ○ NOT HUNGRY

_____

_____

TOTAL CALORIES OR SERVINGS _____

MIDAFTERNOON SNACK: TIME_____   ○ HUNGRY   ○ NOT HUNGRY

_____

TOTAL CALORIES OR SERVINGS _____

DINNER: TIME_____   ○ HUNGRY   ○ NOT HUNGRY

_____

_____

TOTAL CALORIES OR SERVINGS _____

NIGHTTIME SNACK: TIME_____   ○ HUNGRY   ○ NOT HUNGRY

_____

TOTAL CALORIES OR SERVINGS _____

DATE: _____

TIME WALKING: _____

TIME RUNNING: _____

TOTAL WORKOUT TIME: _____

COURSE: _____

_____

RATE HOW YOU FELT (1 being the worst and 10 being the best):

1   2   3   4   5   6   7   8   9   10

OTHER PHYSICAL ACTIVITY: _____

_____

NOTES (weather, injuries, etc.): _____

_____

_____

_____

_____

_____

_____

_____

FOOD LOG
STAGE 5 : DAY 2

BREAKFAST: TIME_____   ○ HUNGRY   ○ NOT HUNGRY

_____

_____

TOTAL CALORIES OR SERVINGS _____

MIDMORNING SNACK: TIME_____   ○ HUNGRY   ○ NOT HUNGRY

_____

TOTAL CALORIES OR SERVINGS _____

LUNCH: TIME_____   ○ HUNGRY   ○ NOT HUNGRY

_____

_____

TOTAL CALORIES OR SERVINGS _____

MIDAFTERNOON SNACK: TIME_____   ○ HUNGRY   ○ NOT HUNGRY

_____

TOTAL CALORIES OR SERVINGS _____

DINNER: TIME_____   ○ HUNGRY   ○ NOT HUNGRY

_____

_____

TOTAL CALORIES OR SERVINGS _____

NIGHTTIME SNACK: TIME_____   ○ HUNGRY   ○ NOT HUNGRY

_____

TOTAL CALORIES OR SERVINGS _____

DATE: _____

TIME WALKING: _____

TIME RUNNING: _____

TOTAL WORKOUT TIME: _____

COURSE: _____

_____

RATE HOW YOU FELT (1 being the worst and 10 being the best):

1   2   3   4   5   6   7   8   9   10

OTHER PHYSICAL ACTIVITY: _____

_____

NOTES (weather, injuries, etc.): _____

_____

_____

_____

_____

_____

_____

_____

FOOD LOG
STAGE 5 : DAY 3

BREAKFAST: TIME_____   ○ HUNGRY   ○ NOT HUNGRY

_____

_____

TOTAL CALORIES OR SERVINGS _____

MIDMORNING SNACK: TIME_____   ○ HUNGRY   ○ NOT HUNGRY

_____

TOTAL CALORIES OR SERVINGS _____

LUNCH: TIME_____   ○ HUNGRY   ○ NOT HUNGRY

_____

_____

TOTAL CALORIES OR SERVINGS _____

MIDAFTERNOON SNACK: TIME_____   ○ HUNGRY   ○ NOT HUNGRY

_____

TOTAL CALORIES OR SERVINGS _____

DINNER: TIME_____   ○ HUNGRY   ○ NOT HUNGRY

_____

_____

TOTAL CALORIES OR SERVINGS _____

NIGHTTIME SNACK: TIME_____   ○ HUNGRY   ○ NOT HUNGRY

_____

TOTAL CALORIES OR SERVINGS _____

WORKOUT
STAGE 5 : DAY 4

DATE: _____

TIME WALKING: _____

TIME RUNNING: _____

TOTAL WORKOUT TIME: _____

COURSE: _____

_____

RATE HOW YOU FELT (1 being the worst and 10 being the best):

1   2   3   4   5   6   7   8   9   10

OTHER PHYSICAL ACTIVITY: _____

_____

NOTES (weather, injuries, etc.): _____

_____

_____

_____

_____

_____

_____

_____

_____

FOOD LOG
STAGE 5 : DAY 4

BREAKFAST: TIME_____   ○ HUNGRY   ○ NOT HUNGRY

_____

_____

TOTAL CALORIES OR SERVINGS _____

MIDMORNING SNACK: TIME_____   ○ HUNGRY   ○ NOT HUNGRY

_____

TOTAL CALORIES OR SERVINGS _____

LUNCH: TIME_____   ○ HUNGRY   ○ NOT HUNGRY

_____

_____

TOTAL CALORIES OR SERVINGS _____

MIDAFTERNOON SNACK: TIME_____   ○ HUNGRY   ○ NOT HUNGRY

_____

TOTAL CALORIES OR SERVINGS _____

DINNER: TIME_____   ○ HUNGRY   ○ NOT HUNGRY

_____

_____

TOTAL CALORIES OR SERVINGS _____

NIGHTTIME SNACK: TIME_____   ○ HUNGRY   ○ NOT HUNGRY

_____

TOTAL CALORIES OR SERVINGS _____

WORKOUT
STAGE 5 : DAY 5

DATE: _____

TIME WALKING: _____

TIME RUNNING: _____

TOTAL WORKOUT TIME: _____

COURSE: _____

_____

RATE HOW YOU FELT (1 being the worst and 10 being the best):

1   2   3   4   5   6   7   8   9   10

OTHER PHYSICAL ACTIVITY: _____

_____

NOTES (weather, injuries, etc.): _____

_____

_____

_____

_____

_____

_____

FOOD LOG
STAGE 5 : DAY 5

BREAKFAST: TIME_____   ○ HUNGRY   ○ NOT HUNGRY

_____

_____

TOTAL CALORIES OR SERVINGS _____

MIDMORNING SNACK: TIME_____   ○ HUNGRY   ○ NOT HUNGRY

_____

TOTAL CALORIES OR SERVINGS _____

LUNCH: TIME_____   ○ HUNGRY   ○ NOT HUNGRY

_____

_____

TOTAL CALORIES OR SERVINGS _____

MIDAFTERNOON SNACK: TIME_____   ○ HUNGRY   ○ NOT HUNGRY

_____

TOTAL CALORIES OR SERVINGS _____

DINNER: TIME_____   ○ HUNGRY   ○ NOT HUNGRY

_____

_____

TOTAL CALORIES OR SERVINGS _____

NIGHTTIME SNACK: TIME_____   ○ HUNGRY   ○ NOT HUNGRY

_____

TOTAL CALORIES OR SERVINGS _____

WORKOUT
STAGE 5 : DAY 6

DATE: _____

TIME WALKING: _____

TIME RUNNING: _____

TOTAL WORKOUT TIME: _____

COURSE: _____

_____

RATE HOW YOU FELT (1 being the worst and 10 being the best):

1   2   3   4   5   6   7   8   9   10

OTHER PHYSICAL ACTIVITY: _____

_____

NOTES (weather, injuries, etc.): _____

_____

_____

_____

_____

_____

_____

_____

FOOD LOG
STAGE 5 : DAY 6

BREAKFAST: TIME_____   ○ HUNGRY   ○ NOT HUNGRY

_____

_____

TOTAL CALORIES OR SERVINGS _____

MIDMORNING SNACK: TIME_____   ○ HUNGRY   ○ NOT HUNGRY

_____

TOTAL CALORIES OR SERVINGS _____

LUNCH: TIME_____   ○ HUNGRY   ○ NOT HUNGRY

_____

_____

TOTAL CALORIES OR SERVINGS _____

MIDAFTERNOON SNACK: TIME_____   ○ HUNGRY   ○ NOT HUNGRY

_____

TOTAL CALORIES OR SERVINGS _____

DINNER: TIME_____   ○ HUNGRY   ○ NOT HUNGRY

_____

_____

TOTAL CALORIES OR SERVINGS _____

NIGHTTIME SNACK: TIME_____   ○ HUNGRY   ○ NOT HUNGRY

_____

TOTAL CALORIES OR SERVINGS _____

WORKOUT
STAGE 5 : DAY 7

DATE: _____

TIME WALKING: _____

TIME RUNNING: _____

TOTAL WORKOUT TIME: _____

COURSE: _____

_____

RATE HOW YOU FELT (1 being the worst and 10 being the best):

1   2   3   4   5   6   7   8   9   10

OTHER PHYSICAL ACTIVITY: _____

_____

NOTES (weather, injuries, etc.): _____

_____

_____

_____

_____

_____

_____

_____

FOOD LOG
STAGE 5 : DAY 7

BREAKFAST: TIME_____　　　　　○ HUNGRY　○ NOT HUNGRY

_____

_____

TOTAL CALORIES OR SERVINGS _____

MIDMORNING SNACK: TIME_____　　　○ HUNGRY　○ NOT HUNGRY

_____

TOTAL CALORIES OR SERVINGS _____

LUNCH: TIME_____　　　　　　　○ HUNGRY　○ NOT HUNGRY

_____

_____

TOTAL CALORIES OR SERVINGS _____

MIDAFTERNOON SNACK: TIME_____　　○ HUNGRY　○ NOT HUNGRY

_____

TOTAL CALORIES OR SERVINGS _____

DINNER: TIME_____　　　　　　○ HUNGRY　○ NOT HUNGRY

_____

_____

TOTAL CALORIES OR SERVINGS _____

NIGHTTIME SNACK: TIME_____　　　○ HUNGRY　○ NOT HUNGRY

_____

TOTAL CALORIES OR SERVINGS _____

Stage 5 CHECK-IN

WEIGHT_____

CHEST_____

WAIST_____

HIPS (AT FULLEST PART)_____

LEFT THIGH_____

RIGHT THIGH_____

LEFT BICEPS_____

RIGHT BICEPS_____

THOUGHTS ON THE WORKOUTS: Record the weather, your effort level, aches and pains, challenges, and successes. How hard did it feel?

_____

_____

_____

GOALS UPDATE

GOAL	DEADLINE FOR MEETING IT	MET GOAL/STILL IN PROGRESS

Stage 6

WORKOUT SUMMARY

- Walk for 3 minutes. Run for 7 minutes.
- Repeat that sequence two more times.
- End with 3 minutes of walking.

**Total workout time:
33 MINUTES, 21 of which are running**

Do this workout at least three or four times in a week
before moving on to the next stage.

**BUDD'S
BUZZ**

"Nonwalkers and nonrunners have this sense of physical
exertion being painful. They feel fatigued, and they might
feel some discomfort. But the person who has walked
or run for a long time? That exertion is ecstasy. We feel
like 'Finally! I can get out there and do something
physical!'"

DATE: _____

TIME WALKING: _____

TIME RUNNING: _____

TOTAL WORKOUT TIME: _____

COURSE: _____

_____

RATE HOW YOU FELT (1 being the worst and 10 being the best):

1   2   3   4   5   6   7   8   9   10

OTHER PHYSICAL ACTIVITY: _____

_____

NOTES (weather, injuries, etc.): _____

_____

_____

_____

_____

_____

_____

_____

FOOD LOG
STAGE 6 : DAY 1

BREAKFAST: TIME_____   ○ HUNGRY   ○ NOT HUNGRY

_____

_____

TOTAL CALORIES OR SERVINGS _____

MIDMORNING SNACK: TIME_____   ○ HUNGRY   ○ NOT HUNGRY

_____

TOTAL CALORIES OR SERVINGS _____

LUNCH: TIME_____   ○ HUNGRY   ○ NOT HUNGRY

_____

_____

TOTAL CALORIES OR SERVINGS _____

MIDAFTERNOON SNACK: TIME_____   ○ HUNGRY   ○ NOT HUNGRY

_____

TOTAL CALORIES OR SERVINGS _____

DINNER: TIME_____   ○ HUNGRY   ○ NOT HUNGRY

_____

_____

TOTAL CALORIES OR SERVINGS _____

NIGHTTIME SNACK: TIME_____   ○ HUNGRY   ○ NOT HUNGRY

_____

TOTAL CALORIES OR SERVINGS _____

WORKOUT
STAGE 6 : DAY 2

DATE: _____

TIME WALKING: _____

TIME RUNNING: _____

TOTAL WORKOUT TIME: _____

COURSE: _____

_____

RATE HOW YOU FELT (1 being the worst and 10 being the best):

1   2   3   4   5   6   7   8   9   10

OTHER PHYSICAL ACTIVITY: _____

_____

NOTES (weather, injuries, etc.): _____

_____

_____

_____

_____

_____

_____

_____

_____

FOOD LOG
STAGE 6 : DAY 2

BREAKFAST: TIME_____   ○ HUNGRY   ○ NOT HUNGRY

_____

_____

TOTAL CALORIES OR SERVINGS _____

MIDMORNING SNACK: TIME_____   ○ HUNGRY   ○ NOT HUNGRY

_____

TOTAL CALORIES OR SERVINGS _____

LUNCH: TIME_____   ○ HUNGRY   ○ NOT HUNGRY

_____

_____

TOTAL CALORIES OR SERVINGS _____

MIDAFTERNOON SNACK: TIME_____   ○ HUNGRY   ○ NOT HUNGRY

_____

TOTAL CALORIES OR SERVINGS _____

DINNER: TIME_____   ○ HUNGRY   ○ NOT HUNGRY

_____

_____

TOTAL CALORIES OR SERVINGS _____

NIGHTTIME SNACK: TIME_____   ○ HUNGRY   ○ NOT HUNGRY

_____

TOTAL CALORIES OR SERVINGS _____

Run Your Butt Off!

WORKOUT
STAGE 6 : DAY 3

DATE: _____

TIME WALKING: _____

TIME RUNNING: _____

TOTAL WORKOUT TIME: _____

COURSE: _____

_____

RATE HOW YOU FELT (1 being the worst and 10 being the best):

1   2   3   4   5   6   7   8   9   10

OTHER PHYSICAL ACTIVITY: _____

_____

NOTES (weather, injuries, etc.): _____

_____

_____

_____

_____

_____

_____

_____

FOOD LOG
STAGE 6 : DAY 3

BREAKFAST: TIME_____   ○ HUNGRY   ○ NOT HUNGRY

_____

_____

TOTAL CALORIES OR SERVINGS _____

MIDMORNING SNACK: TIME_____   ○ HUNGRY   ○ NOT HUNGRY

_____

TOTAL CALORIES OR SERVINGS _____

LUNCH: TIME_____   ○ HUNGRY   ○ NOT HUNGRY

_____

_____

TOTAL CALORIES OR SERVINGS _____

MIDAFTERNOON SNACK: TIME_____   ○ HUNGRY   ○ NOT HUNGRY

_____

TOTAL CALORIES OR SERVINGS _____

DINNER: TIME_____   ○ HUNGRY   ○ NOT HUNGRY

_____

_____

TOTAL CALORIES OR SERVINGS _____

NIGHTTIME SNACK: TIME_____   ○ HUNGRY   ○ NOT HUNGRY

_____

TOTAL CALORIES OR SERVINGS _____

WORKOUT
STAGE 6 : DAY 4

DATE: _____

TIME WALKING: _____

TIME RUNNING: _____

TOTAL WORKOUT TIME: _____

COURSE: _____

_____

RATE HOW YOU FELT (1 being the worst and 10 being the best):

1   2   3   4   5   6   7   8   9   10

OTHER PHYSICAL ACTIVITY: _____

_____

NOTES (weather, injuries, etc.): _____

_____

_____

_____

_____

_____

_____

_____

FOOD LOG
STAGE 6 : DAY 4

BREAKFAST: TIME_____   ○ HUNGRY   ○ NOT HUNGRY

_____

_____

TOTAL CALORIES OR SERVINGS _____

MIDMORNING SNACK: TIME_____   ○ HUNGRY   ○ NOT HUNGRY

_____

TOTAL CALORIES OR SERVINGS _____

LUNCH: TIME_____   ○ HUNGRY   ○ NOT HUNGRY

_____

_____

TOTAL CALORIES OR SERVINGS _____

MIDAFTERNOON SNACK: TIME_____   ○ HUNGRY   ○ NOT HUNGRY

_____

TOTAL CALORIES OR SERVINGS _____

DINNER: TIME_____   ○ HUNGRY   ○ NOT HUNGRY

_____

_____

TOTAL CALORIES OR SERVINGS _____

NIGHTTIME SNACK: TIME_____   ○ HUNGRY   ○ NOT HUNGRY

_____

TOTAL CALORIES OR SERVINGS _____

WORKOUT
STAGE 6 : DAY 5

DATE: _____

TIME WALKING: _____

TIME RUNNING: _____

TOTAL WORKOUT TIME: _____

COURSE: _____

_____

RATE HOW YOU FELT (1 being the worst and 10 being the best):

1   2   3   4   5   6   7   8   9   10

OTHER PHYSICAL ACTIVITY: _____

_____

NOTES (weather, injuries, etc.): _____

_____

_____

_____

_____

_____

_____

_____

FOOD LOG
STAGE 6 : DAY 5

BREAKFAST: TIME_____   ○ HUNGRY   ○ NOT HUNGRY

TOTAL CALORIES OR SERVINGS _____

MIDMORNING SNACK: TIME_____   ○ HUNGRY   ○ NOT HUNGRY

TOTAL CALORIES OR SERVINGS _____

LUNCH: TIME_____   ○ HUNGRY   ○ NOT HUNGRY

TOTAL CALORIES OR SERVINGS _____

MIDAFTERNOON SNACK: TIME_____   ○ HUNGRY   ○ NOT HUNGRY

TOTAL CALORIES OR SERVINGS _____

DINNER: TIME_____   ○ HUNGRY   ○ NOT HUNGRY

TOTAL CALORIES OR SERVINGS _____

NIGHTTIME SNACK: TIME_____   ○ HUNGRY   ○ NOT HUNGRY

TOTAL CALORIES OR SERVINGS _____

WORKOUT
STAGE 6 : DAY 6

DATE: _____

TIME WALKING: _____

TIME RUNNING: _____

TOTAL WORKOUT TIME: _____

COURSE: _____

_____

RATE HOW YOU FELT (1 being the worst and 10 being the best):

1   2   3   4   5   6   7   8   9   10

OTHER PHYSICAL ACTIVITY: _____

_____

NOTES (weather, injuries, etc.): _____

_____

_____

_____

_____

_____

_____

_____

FOOD LOG
STAGE 6 : DAY 6

BREAKFAST: TIME_____   ○ HUNGRY   ○ NOT HUNGRY

_____

_____

TOTAL CALORIES OR SERVINGS _____

MIDMORNING SNACK: TIME_____   ○ HUNGRY   ○ NOT HUNGRY

_____

TOTAL CALORIES OR SERVINGS _____

LUNCH: TIME_____   ○ HUNGRY   ○ NOT HUNGRY

_____

_____

TOTAL CALORIES OR SERVINGS _____

MIDAFTERNOON SNACK: TIME_____   ○ HUNGRY   ○ NOT HUNGRY

_____

TOTAL CALORIES OR SERVINGS _____

DINNER: TIME_____   ○ HUNGRY   ○ NOT HUNGRY

_____

_____

TOTAL CALORIES OR SERVINGS _____

NIGHTTIME SNACK: TIME_____   ○ HUNGRY   ○ NOT HUNGRY

_____

TOTAL CALORIES OR SERVINGS _____

Run Your Butt Off!

WORKOUT
STAGE 6 : DAY 7

DATE: _____

TIME WALKING: _____

TIME RUNNING: _____

TOTAL WORKOUT TIME: _____

COURSE: _____

_____

RATE HOW YOU FELT (1 being the worst and 10 being the best):

1   2   3   4   5   6   7   8   9   10

OTHER PHYSICAL ACTIVITY: _____

_____

NOTES (weather, injuries, etc.): _____

_____

_____

_____

_____

_____

_____

_____

FOOD LOG
STAGE 6 : DAY 7

BREAKFAST: TIME_____   ○ HUNGRY   ○ NOT HUNGRY

_____

_____

TOTAL CALORIES OR SERVINGS _____

MIDMORNING SNACK: TIME_____   ○ HUNGRY   ○ NOT HUNGRY

_____

TOTAL CALORIES OR SERVINGS _____

LUNCH: TIME_____   ○ HUNGRY   ○ NOT HUNGRY

_____

_____

TOTAL CALORIES OR SERVINGS _____

MIDAFTERNOON SNACK: TIME_____   ○ HUNGRY   ○ NOT HUNGRY

_____

TOTAL CALORIES OR SERVINGS _____

DINNER: TIME_____   ○ HUNGRY   ○ NOT HUNGRY

_____

_____

TOTAL CALORIES OR SERVINGS _____

NIGHTTIME SNACK: TIME_____   ○ HUNGRY   ○ NOT HUNGRY

_____

TOTAL CALORIES OR SERVINGS _____

Stage 6 CHECK-IN

WEIGHT_____

CHEST_____

WAIST_____

HIPS (AT FULLEST PART)_____

LEFT THIGH_____

RIGHT THIGH_____

LEFT BICEPS_____

RIGHT BICEPS_____

THOUGHTS ON THE WORKOUTS: Record the weather, your effort level, aches and pains, challenges, and successes. How hard did it feel?

_____

_____

_____

GOALS UPDATE

GOAL	DEADLINE FOR MEETING IT	MET GOAL/STILL IN PROGRESS

Stage 7
WORKOUT SUMMARY

- Walk for 2 minutes. Run for 8 minutes.
- Repeat that sequence two more times.
- End with 3 minutes of walking.

**Total workout time:
33 MINUTES, 24 of which are running**

Do this workout at least three or four times in a week
before moving on to the next stage.

**BUDD'S
BUZZ**

"You are the best judge of how you feel. Don't keep
pushing through an injury just because you want to get
in that last workout of the week or you want to do that
race. Better to modify your training program with a
couple of extra days off or go back to a little more
walking, a little less running, than to be completely
derailed by an injury. Usually it's the 'just one more day'
mentality that gets people into trouble. 'Let me do my
workout today, and then I'll take some time off.' But by
then the damage is done."

DATE: _____

TIME WALKING: _____

TIME RUNNING: _____

TOTAL WORKOUT TIME: _____

COURSE: _____

_____

RATE HOW YOU FELT (1 being the worst and 10 being the best):

1   2   3   4   5   6   7   8   9   10

OTHER PHYSICAL ACTIVITY: _____

_____

NOTES (weather, injuries, etc.): _____

_____

_____

_____

_____

_____

_____

_____

FOOD LOG
STAGE 7 : DAY 1

BREAKFAST: TIME_____   ○ HUNGRY   ○ NOT HUNGRY

_____

_____

TOTAL CALORIES OR SERVINGS _____

MIDMORNING SNACK: TIME_____   ○ HUNGRY   ○ NOT HUNGRY

_____

TOTAL CALORIES OR SERVINGS _____

LUNCH: TIME_____   ○ HUNGRY   ○ NOT HUNGRY

_____

_____

TOTAL CALORIES OR SERVINGS _____

MIDAFTERNOON SNACK: TIME_____   ○ HUNGRY   ○ NOT HUNGRY

_____

TOTAL CALORIES OR SERVINGS _____

DINNER: TIME_____   ○ HUNGRY   ○ NOT HUNGRY

_____

_____

TOTAL CALORIES OR SERVINGS _____

NIGHTTIME SNACK: TIME_____   ○ HUNGRY   ○ NOT HUNGRY

_____

TOTAL CALORIES OR SERVINGS _____

WORKOUT
STAGE 7 : DAY 2

DATE: _____

TIME WALKING: _____

TIME RUNNING: _____

TOTAL WORKOUT TIME: _____

COURSE: _____

_____

RATE HOW YOU FELT (1 being the worst and 10 being the best):

1   2   3   4   5   6   7   8   9   10

OTHER PHYSICAL ACTIVITY: _____

_____

NOTES (weather, injuries, etc.): _____

_____

_____

_____

_____

_____

_____

_____

FOOD LOG
STAGE 7 : DAY 2

BREAKFAST: TIME_____   ○ HUNGRY   ○ NOT HUNGRY

_____

_____

TOTAL CALORIES OR SERVINGS _____

MIDMORNING SNACK: TIME_____   ○ HUNGRY   ○ NOT HUNGRY

_____

TOTAL CALORIES OR SERVINGS _____

LUNCH: TIME_____   ○ HUNGRY   ○ NOT HUNGRY

_____

_____

TOTAL CALORIES OR SERVINGS _____

MIDAFTERNOON SNACK: TIME_____   ○ HUNGRY   ○ NOT HUNGRY

_____

TOTAL CALORIES OR SERVINGS _____

DINNER: TIME_____   ○ HUNGRY   ○ NOT HUNGRY

_____

_____

TOTAL CALORIES OR SERVINGS _____

NIGHTTIME SNACK: TIME_____ .   ○ HUNGRY   ○ NOT HUNGRY

_____

TOTAL CALORIES OR SERVINGS _____

Run Your Butt Off!

WORKOUT
STAGE 7 : DAY 3

DATE: _____

TIME WALKING: _____

TIME RUNNING: _____

TOTAL WORKOUT TIME: _____

COURSE: _____

_____

RATE HOW YOU FELT (1 being the worst and 10 being the best):

1   2   3   4   5   6   7   8   9   10

OTHER PHYSICAL ACTIVITY: _____

_____

NOTES (weather, injuries, etc.): _____

_____

_____

_____

_____

_____

_____

FOOD LOG
STAGE 7 : DAY 3

BREAKFAST: TIME_____   ○ HUNGRY   ○ NOT HUNGRY

_____

_____

TOTAL CALORIES OR SERVINGS _____

MIDMORNING SNACK: TIME_____   ○ HUNGRY   ○ NOT HUNGRY

_____

TOTAL CALORIES OR SERVINGS _____

LUNCH: TIME_____   ○ HUNGRY   ○ NOT HUNGRY

_____

_____

TOTAL CALORIES OR SERVINGS _____

MIDAFTERNOON SNACK: TIME_____   ○ HUNGRY   ○ NOT HUNGRY

_____

TOTAL CALORIES OR SERVINGS _____

DINNER: TIME_____   ○ HUNGRY   ○ NOT HUNGRY

_____

_____

TOTAL CALORIES OR SERVINGS _____

NIGHTTIME SNACK: TIME_____   ○ HUNGRY   ○ NOT HUNGRY

_____

TOTAL CALORIES OR SERVINGS _____

WORKOUT
STAGE 7 : DAY 4

DATE: _____

TIME WALKING: _____

TIME RUNNING: _____

TOTAL WORKOUT TIME: _____

COURSE: _____

_____

RATE HOW YOU FELT (1 being the worst and 10 being the best):

1   2   3   4   5   6   7   8   9   10

OTHER PHYSICAL ACTIVITY: _____

_____

NOTES (weather, injuries, etc.): _____

_____

_____

_____

_____

_____

_____

FOOD LOG
STAGE 7 : DAY 4

BREAKFAST: TIME_____   ○ HUNGRY   ○ NOT HUNGRY

_____

_____

TOTAL CALORIES OR SERVINGS _____

MIDMORNING SNACK: TIME_____   ○ HUNGRY   ○ NOT HUNGRY

_____

TOTAL CALORIES OR SERVINGS _____

LUNCH: TIME_____   ○ HUNGRY   ○ NOT HUNGRY

_____

_____

TOTAL CALORIES OR SERVINGS _____

MIDAFTERNOON SNACK: TIME_____   ○ HUNGRY   ○ NOT HUNGRY

_____

TOTAL CALORIES OR SERVINGS _____

DINNER: TIME_____   ○ HUNGRY   ○ NOT HUNGRY

_____

_____

TOTAL CALORIES OR SERVINGS _____

NIGHTTIME SNACK: TIME_____   ○ HUNGRY   ○ NOT HUNGRY

_____

TOTAL CALORIES OR SERVINGS _____

DATE: _____

TIME WALKING: _____

TIME RUNNING: _____

TOTAL WORKOUT TIME: _____

COURSE: _____

_____

RATE HOW YOU FELT (1 being the worst and 10 being the best):

1   2   3   4   5   6   7   8   9   10

OTHER PHYSICAL ACTIVITY: _____

_____

NOTES (weather, injuries, etc.): _____

_____

_____

_____

_____

_____

_____

FOOD LOG
STAGE 7 : DAY 5

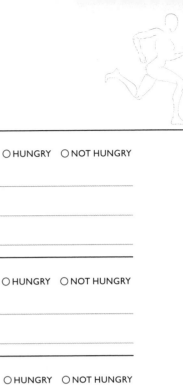

BREAKFAST: TIME_____   ○ HUNGRY   ○ NOT HUNGRY

_____

_____

TOTAL CALORIES OR SERVINGS _____

MIDMORNING SNACK: TIME_____   ○ HUNGRY   ○ NOT HUNGRY

_____

TOTAL CALORIES OR SERVINGS _____

LUNCH: TIME_____   ○ HUNGRY   ○ NOT HUNGRY

_____

_____

TOTAL CALORIES OR SERVINGS _____

MIDAFTERNOON SNACK: TIME_____   ○ HUNGRY   ○ NOT HUNGRY

_____

TOTAL CALORIES OR SERVINGS _____

DINNER: TIME_____   ○ HUNGRY   ○ NOT HUNGRY

_____

_____

TOTAL CALORIES OR SERVINGS _____

NIGHTTIME SNACK: TIME_____   ○ HUNGRY   ○ NOT HUNGRY

_____

TOTAL CALORIES OR SERVINGS _____

WORKOUT
STAGE 7 : DAY 6

DATE: _____

TIME WALKING: _____

TIME RUNNING: _____

TOTAL WORKOUT TIME: _____

COURSE: _____

_____

RATE HOW YOU FELT (1 being the worst and 10 being the best):

1   2   3   4   5   6   7   8   9   10

OTHER PHYSICAL ACTIVITY: _____

_____

NOTES (weather, injuries, etc.): _____

_____

_____

_____

_____

_____

_____

_____

FOOD LOG
STAGE 7 : DAY 6

BREAKFAST: TIME_____   ○ HUNGRY   ○ NOT HUNGRY

_____

_____

TOTAL CALORIES OR SERVINGS _____

MIDMORNING SNACK: TIME_____   ○ HUNGRY   ○ NOT HUNGRY

_____

TOTAL CALORIES OR SERVINGS _____

LUNCH: TIME_____   ○ HUNGRY   ○ NOT HUNGRY

_____

_____

TOTAL CALORIES OR SERVINGS _____

MIDAFTERNOON SNACK: TIME_____   ○ HUNGRY   ○ NOT HUNGRY

_____

TOTAL CALORIES OR SERVINGS _____

DINNER: TIME_____   ○ HUNGRY   ○ NOT HUNGRY

_____

_____

TOTAL CALORIES OR SERVINGS _____

NIGHTTIME SNACK: TIME_____   ○ HUNGRY   ○ NOT HUNGRY

_____

TOTAL CALORIES OR SERVINGS _____

WORKOUT
STAGE 7 : DAY 7

DATE: _____

TIME WALKING: _____

TIME RUNNING: _____

TOTAL WORKOUT TIME: _____

COURSE: _____

_____

RATE HOW YOU FELT (1 being the worst and 10 being the best):

1   2   3   4   5   6   7   8   9   10

OTHER PHYSICAL ACTIVITY: _____

_____

NOTES (weather, injuries, etc.): _____

_____

_____

_____

_____

_____

_____

_____

FOOD LOG
STAGE 7 : DAY 7

BREAKFAST: TIME_____   ○ HUNGRY   ○ NOT HUNGRY

_____

_____

TOTAL CALORIES OR SERVINGS _____

MIDMORNING SNACK: TIME_____   ○ HUNGRY   ○ NOT HUNGRY

_____

TOTAL CALORIES OR SERVINGS _____

LUNCH: TIME_____   ○ HUNGRY   ○ NOT HUNGRY

_____

_____

TOTAL CALORIES OR SERVINGS _____

MIDAFTERNOON SNACK: TIME_____   ○ HUNGRY   ○ NOT HUNGRY

_____

TOTAL CALORIES OR SERVINGS _____

DINNER: TIME_____   ○ HUNGRY   ○ NOT HUNGRY

_____

_____

TOTAL CALORIES OR SERVINGS _____

NIGHTTIME SNACK: TIME_____   ○ HUNGRY   ○ NOT HUNGRY

_____

TOTAL CALORIES OR SERVINGS _____

Stage 7 CHECK-IN

WEIGHT_____

CHEST_____

WAIST_____

HIPS (AT FULLEST PART)_____

LEFT THIGH_____

RIGHT THIGH_____

LEFT BICEPS_____

RIGHT BICEPS_____

THOUGHTS ON THE WORKOUTS: Record the weather, your effort level, aches and pains, challenges, and successes. How hard did it feel?

_____

_____

_____

GOALS UPDATE

GOAL	DEADLINE FOR MEETING IT	MET GOAL/STILL IN PROGRESS

Stage 8
WORKOUT SUMMARY

- Walk for 2 minutes. Run for 9 minutes.
- Repeat that sequence one more time.
- Then walk for 2 minutes, run for 8 minutes.
- End with 3 minutes of walking.

**Total workout time:
35 MINUTES, 26 of which are running**

Do this workout at least three or four times in a week
before moving on to the next stage.

**BUDD'S
BUZZ**

"By the time you run for 8 minutes, you might not be
able to see off in the distance how far you're going.
And your mind starts to drift. And that's when it's
pretty cool. You don't have to concentrate on 'I'm
running, I'm running' the whole time. You can let
yourself daydream, solve a few problems. You don't
have to keep looking at your watch because you know
that it's going to be a while."

Run Your Butt Off!

WORKOUT
STAGE 8 : DAY 1

DATE: _____

TIME WALKING: _____

TIME RUNNING: _____

TOTAL WORKOUT TIME: _____

COURSE: _____

_____

RATE HOW YOU FELT (1 being the worst and 10 being the best):

1   2   3   4   5   6   7   8   9   10

OTHER PHYSICAL ACTIVITY: _____

_____

NOTES (weather, injuries, etc.): _____

_____

_____

_____

_____

_____

_____

_____

FOOD LOG
STAGE 8 : DAY 1

BREAKFAST: TIME_____   ○ HUNGRY   ○ NOT HUNGRY

_____

_____

TOTAL CALORIES OR SERVINGS _____

MIDMORNING SNACK: TIME_____   ○ HUNGRY   ○ NOT HUNGRY

_____

TOTAL CALORIES OR SERVINGS _____

LUNCH: TIME_____   ○ HUNGRY   ○ NOT HUNGRY

_____

_____

TOTAL CALORIES OR SERVINGS _____

MIDAFTERNOON SNACK: TIME_____   ○ HUNGRY   ○ NOT HUNGRY

_____

TOTAL CALORIES OR SERVINGS _____

DINNER: TIME_____   ○ HUNGRY   ○ NOT HUNGRY

_____

_____

TOTAL CALORIES OR SERVINGS _____

NIGHTTIME SNACK: TIME_____   ○ HUNGRY   ○ NOT HUNGRY

_____

TOTAL CALORIES OR SERVINGS _____

DATE: _____

TIME WALKING: _____

TIME RUNNING: _____

TOTAL WORKOUT TIME: _____

COURSE: _____

_____

RATE HOW YOU FELT (1 being the worst and 10 being the best):

1   2   3   4   5   6   7   8   9   10

OTHER PHYSICAL ACTIVITY: _____

_____

NOTES (weather, injuries, etc.): _____

_____

_____

_____

_____

_____

_____

_____

FOOD LOG
STAGE 8 : DAY 2

BREAKFAST: TIME_____   ○ HUNGRY   ○ NOT HUNGRY

_____

_____

TOTAL CALORIES OR SERVINGS _____

MIDMORNING SNACK: TIME_____   ○ HUNGRY   ○ NOT HUNGRY

_____

TOTAL CALORIES OR SERVINGS _____

LUNCH: TIME_____   ○ HUNGRY   ○ NOT HUNGRY

_____

_____

TOTAL CALORIES OR SERVINGS _____

MIDAFTERNOON SNACK: TIME_____   ○ HUNGRY   ○ NOT HUNGRY

_____

TOTAL CALORIES OR SERVINGS _____

DINNER: TIME_____   ○ HUNGRY   ○ NOT HUNGRY

_____

_____

TOTAL CALORIES OR SERVINGS _____

NIGHTTIME SNACK: TIME_____   ○ HUNGRY   ○ NOT HUNGRY

_____

TOTAL CALORIES OR SERVINGS _____

WORKOUT
STAGE 8 : DAY 3

DATE: _____

TIME WALKING: _____

TIME RUNNING: _____

TOTAL WORKOUT TIME: _____

COURSE: _____

_____

RATE HOW YOU FELT (1 being the worst and 10 being the best):

1   2   3   4   5   6   7   8   9   10

OTHER PHYSICAL ACTIVITY: _____

_____

NOTES (weather, injuries, etc.): _____

_____

_____

_____

_____

_____

_____

_____

FOOD LOG
STAGE 8 : DAY 3

BREAKFAST: TIME_____   ○ HUNGRY   ○ NOT HUNGRY

_____

_____

TOTAL CALORIES OR SERVINGS _____

MIDMORNING SNACK: TIME_____   ○ HUNGRY   ○ NOT HUNGRY

_____

TOTAL CALORIES OR SERVINGS _____

LUNCH: TIME_____   ○ HUNGRY   ○ NOT HUNGRY

_____

_____

TOTAL CALORIES OR SERVINGS _____

MIDAFTERNOON SNACK: TIME_____   ○ HUNGRY   ○ NOT HUNGRY

_____

TOTAL CALORIES OR SERVINGS _____

DINNER: TIME_____   ○ HUNGRY   ○ NOT HUNGRY

_____

_____

TOTAL CALORIES OR SERVINGS _____

NIGHTTIME SNACK: TIME_____   ○ HUNGRY   ○ NOT HUNGRY

_____

TOTAL CALORIES OR SERVINGS _____

WORKOUT
STAGE 8 : DAY 4

DATE: _____

TIME WALKING: _____

TIME RUNNING: _____

TOTAL WORKOUT TIME: _____

COURSE: _____

_____

RATE HOW YOU FELT (1 being the worst and 10 being the best):

| 1 | 2 | 3 | 4 | 5 | 6 | 7 | 8 | 9 | 10 |

OTHER PHYSICAL ACTIVITY: _____

_____

NOTES (weather, injuries, etc.): _____

_____

_____

_____

_____

_____

_____

_____

_____

FOOD LOG
STAGE 8 : DAY 4

BREAKFAST: TIME_____   ○ HUNGRY   ○ NOT HUNGRY

_____

_____

TOTAL CALORIES OR SERVINGS _____

MIDMORNING SNACK: TIME_____   ○ HUNGRY   ○ NOT HUNGRY

_____

TOTAL CALORIES OR SERVINGS _____

LUNCH: TIME_____   ○ HUNGRY   ○ NOT HUNGRY

_____

_____

TOTAL CALORIES OR SERVINGS _____

MIDAFTERNOON SNACK: TIME_____   ○ HUNGRY   ○ NOT HUNGRY

_____

TOTAL CALORIES OR SERVINGS _____

DINNER: TIME_____   ○ HUNGRY   ○ NOT HUNGRY

_____

_____

TOTAL CALORIES OR SERVINGS _____

NIGHTTIME SNACK: TIME_____   ○ HUNGRY   ○ NOT HUNGRY

_____

TOTAL CALORIES OR SERVINGS _____

WORKOUT
STAGE 8 : DAY 5

DATE: _____

TIME WALKING: _____

TIME RUNNING: _____

TOTAL WORKOUT TIME: _____

COURSE: _____

_____

RATE HOW YOU FELT (1 being the worst and 10 being the best):

1   2   3   4   5   6   7   8   9   10

OTHER PHYSICAL ACTIVITY: _____

_____

NOTES (weather, injuries, etc.): _____

_____

_____

_____

_____

_____

_____

_____

_____

FOOD LOG
STAGE 8 : DAY 5

BREAKFAST: TIME_____   ○ HUNGRY   ○ NOT HUNGRY

_____

_____

TOTAL CALORIES OR SERVINGS _____

MIDMORNING SNACK: TIME_____   ○ HUNGRY   ○ NOT HUNGRY

_____

TOTAL CALORIES OR SERVINGS _____

LUNCH: TIME_____   ○ HUNGRY   ○ NOT HUNGRY

_____

_____

TOTAL CALORIES OR SERVINGS _____

MIDAFTERNOON SNACK: TIME_____   ○ HUNGRY   ○ NOT HUNGRY

_____

TOTAL CALORIES OR SERVINGS _____

DINNER: TIME_____   ○ HUNGRY   ○ NOT HUNGRY

_____

_____

TOTAL CALORIES OR SERVINGS _____

NIGHTTIME SNACK: TIME_____   ○ HUNGRY   ○ NOT HUNGRY

_____

TOTAL CALORIES OR SERVINGS _____

WORKOUT
STAGE 8 : DAY 6

DATE: _____

TIME WALKING: _____

TIME RUNNING: _____

TOTAL WORKOUT TIME: _____

COURSE: _____

_____

RATE HOW YOU FELT (1 being the worst and 10 being the best):

1   2   3   4   5   6   7   8   9   10

OTHER PHYSICAL ACTIVITY: _____

_____

NOTES (weather, injuries, etc.): _____

_____

_____

_____

_____

_____

_____

_____

FOOD LOG
STAGE 8 : DAY 6

BREAKFAST: TIME_____   ○ HUNGRY   ○ NOT HUNGRY

_____

_____

TOTAL CALORIES OR SERVINGS _____

MIDMORNING SNACK: TIME_____   ○ HUNGRY   ○ NOT HUNGRY

_____

TOTAL CALORIES OR SERVINGS _____

LUNCH: TIME_____   ○ HUNGRY   ○ NOT HUNGRY

_____

_____

TOTAL CALORIES OR SERVINGS _____

MIDAFTERNOON SNACK: TIME_____   ○ HUNGRY   ○ NOT HUNGRY

_____

TOTAL CALORIES OR SERVINGS _____

DINNER: TIME_____   ○ HUNGRY   ○ NOT HUNGRY

_____

_____

TOTAL CALORIES OR SERVINGS _____

NIGHTTIME SNACK: TIME_____   ○ HUNGRY   ○ NOT HUNGRY

_____

TOTAL CALORIES OR SERVINGS _____

WORKOUT
STAGE 8 : DAY 7

DATE: _____

TIME WALKING: _____

TIME RUNNING: _____

TOTAL WORKOUT TIME: _____

COURSE: _____

_____

RATE HOW YOU FELT (1 being the worst and 10 being the best):

1   2   3   4   5   6   7   8   9   10

OTHER PHYSICAL ACTIVITY: _____

_____

NOTES (weather, injuries, etc.): _____

_____

_____

_____

_____

_____

_____

_____

FOOD LOG
STAGE 8 : DAY 7

BREAKFAST: TIME_____   ○ HUNGRY   ○ NOT HUNGRY

_____

_____

TOTAL CALORIES OR SERVINGS _____

MIDMORNING SNACK: TIME_____   ○ HUNGRY   ○ NOT HUNGRY

_____

TOTAL CALORIES OR SERVINGS _____

LUNCH: TIME_____   ○ HUNGRY   ○ NOT HUNGRY

_____

_____

TOTAL CALORIES OR SERVINGS _____

MIDAFTERNOON SNACK: TIME_____   ○ HUNGRY   ○ NOT HUNGRY

_____

TOTAL CALORIES OR SERVINGS _____

DINNER: TIME_____   ○ HUNGRY   ○ NOT HUNGRY

_____

_____

TOTAL CALORIES OR SERVINGS _____

NIGHTTIME SNACK: TIME_____   ○ HUNGRY   ○ NOT HUNGRY

_____

TOTAL CALORIES OR SERVINGS _____

Stage 8 CHECK-IN

WEIGHT_____

CHEST_____

WAIST_____

HIPS (AT FULLEST PART)_____

LEFT THIGH_____

RIGHT THIGH_____

LEFT BICEPS_____

RIGHT BICEPS_____

THOUGHTS ON THE WORKOUTS: Record the weather, your effort level, aches and pains, challenges, and successes. How hard did it feel?

_____

_____

_____

GOALS UPDATE

GOAL	DEADLINE FOR MEETING IT	MET GOAL/STILL IN PROGRESS

Stage 9
WORKOUT SUMMARY

- Walk for 1 minute. Run for 9 minutes.
- Repeat that sequence two more times.
- End with 3 minutes of walking.

**Total workout time:
33 MINUTES, 27 of which are running**

Do this workout at least three or four times in a week
before moving on to the next stage.

**BUDD'S
BUZZ**

"Every once in a while, I coach a runner and I need to
say, 'You've been at this stage for 3 weeks now; you've
got to move up, let's go!' Those are the people who
need to get an attitude, a nothing-can-stop-me attitude.
Really! Don't give in. Don't settle for less. Set a goal and
accomplish it. Your goal is to run for 30 minutes. Let's
keep going!"

DATE: _____

TIME WALKING: _____

TIME RUNNING: _____

TOTAL WORKOUT TIME: _____

COURSE: _____

_____

RATE HOW YOU FELT (1 being the worst and 10 being the best):

1   2   3   4   5   6   7   8   9   10

OTHER PHYSICAL ACTIVITY: _____

_____

NOTES (weather, injuries, etc.): _____

_____

_____

_____

_____

_____

_____

_____

FOOD LOG
STAGE 9 : DAY 1

BREAKFAST: TIME_____   ○ HUNGRY   ○ NOT HUNGRY

_____

_____

TOTAL CALORIES OR SERVINGS _____

MIDMORNING SNACK: TIME_____   ○ HUNGRY   ○ NOT HUNGRY

_____

TOTAL CALORIES OR SERVINGS _____

LUNCH: TIME_____   ○ HUNGRY   ○ NOT HUNGRY

_____

_____

TOTAL CALORIES OR SERVINGS _____

MIDAFTERNOON SNACK: TIME_____   ○ HUNGRY   ○ NOT HUNGRY

_____

TOTAL CALORIES OR SERVINGS _____

DINNER: TIME_____   ○ HUNGRY   ○ NOT HUNGRY

_____

_____

TOTAL CALORIES OR SERVINGS _____

NIGHTTIME SNACK: TIME_____   ○ HUNGRY   ○ NOT HUNGRY

_____

TOTAL CALORIES OR SERVINGS _____

DATE: _____

TIME WALKING: _____

TIME RUNNING: _____

TOTAL WORKOUT TIME: _____

COURSE: _____

_____

RATE HOW YOU FELT (1 being the worst and 10 being the best):

1   2   3   4   5   6   7   8   9   10

OTHER PHYSICAL ACTIVITY: _____

_____

NOTES (weather, injuries, etc.): _____

_____

_____

_____

_____

_____

_____

_____

FOOD LOG
STAGE 9 : DAY 2

BREAKFAST: TIME_____   ○ HUNGRY   ○ NOT HUNGRY

_____

_____

TOTAL CALORIES OR SERVINGS _____

MIDMORNING SNACK: TIME_____   ○ HUNGRY   ○ NOT HUNGRY

_____

TOTAL CALORIES OR SERVINGS _____

LUNCH: TIME_____   ○ HUNGRY   ○ NOT HUNGRY

_____

_____

TOTAL CALORIES OR SERVINGS _____

MIDAFTERNOON SNACK: TIME_____   ○ HUNGRY   ○ NOT HUNGRY

_____

TOTAL CALORIES OR SERVINGS _____

DINNER: TIME_____   ○ HUNGRY   ○ NOT HUNGRY

_____

_____

TOTAL CALORIES OR SERVINGS _____

NIGHTTIME SNACK: TIME_____   ○ HUNGRY   ○ NOT HUNGRY

_____

TOTAL CALORIES OR SERVINGS _____

Run
Your
Butt
Off!

WORKOUT
STAGE 9 : DAY 3

DATE: _____

TIME WALKING: _____

TIME RUNNING: _____

TOTAL WORKOUT TIME: _____

COURSE: _____

_____

RATE HOW YOU FELT (1 being the worst and 10 being the best):

1   2   3   4   5   6   7   8   9   10

OTHER PHYSICAL ACTIVITY: _____

_____

NOTES (weather, injuries, etc.): _____

_____

_____

_____

_____

_____

_____

_____

FOOD LOG
STAGE 9 : DAY 3

BREAKFAST: TIME_____   ○ HUNGRY   ○ NOT HUNGRY

_____

_____

TOTAL CALORIES OR SERVINGS _____

MIDMORNING SNACK: TIME_____   ○ HUNGRY   ○ NOT HUNGRY

_____

TOTAL CALORIES OR SERVINGS _____

LUNCH: TIME_____   ○ HUNGRY   ○ NOT HUNGRY

_____

_____

TOTAL CALORIES OR SERVINGS _____

MIDAFTERNOON SNACK: TIME_____   ○ HUNGRY   ○ NOT HUNGRY

_____

TOTAL CALORIES OR SERVINGS _____

DINNER: TIME_____   ○ HUNGRY   ○ NOT HUNGRY

_____

_____

TOTAL CALORIES OR SERVINGS _____

NIGHTTIME SNACK: TIME_____   ○ HUNGRY   ○ NOT HUNGRY

_____

TOTAL CALORIES OR SERVINGS _____

DATE: _____

TIME WALKING: _____

TIME RUNNING: _____

TOTAL WORKOUT TIME: _____

COURSE: _____

_____

RATE HOW YOU FELT (1 being the worst and 10 being the best):

1   2   3   4   5   6   7   8   9   10

OTHER PHYSICAL ACTIVITY: _____

_____

NOTES (weather, injuries, etc.): _____

_____

_____

_____

_____

_____

_____

_____

_____

FOOD LOG
STAGE 9 : DAY 4

BREAKFAST: TIME_____   ○ HUNGRY   ○ NOT HUNGRY

_____

_____

TOTAL CALORIES OR SERVINGS _____

MIDMORNING SNACK: TIME_____   ○ HUNGRY   ○ NOT HUNGRY

_____

TOTAL CALORIES OR SERVINGS _____

LUNCH: TIME_____   ○ HUNGRY   ○ NOT HUNGRY

_____

_____

TOTAL CALORIES OR SERVINGS _____

MIDAFTERNOON SNACK: TIME_____   ○ HUNGRY   ○ NOT HUNGRY

_____

TOTAL CALORIES OR SERVINGS _____

DINNER: TIME_____   ○ HUNGRY   ○ NOT HUNGRY

_____

_____

TOTAL CALORIES OR SERVINGS _____

NIGHTTIME SNACK: TIME_____   ○ HUNGRY   ○ NOT HUNGRY

_____

TOTAL CALORIES OR SERVINGS _____

DATE: _____

TIME WALKING: _____

TIME RUNNING: _____

TOTAL WORKOUT TIME: _____

COURSE: _____

_____

RATE HOW YOU FELT (1 being the worst and 10 being the best):

1   2   3   4   5   6   7   8   9   10

OTHER PHYSICAL ACTIVITY: _____

_____

NOTES (weather, injuries, etc.): _____

_____

_____

_____

_____

_____

_____

_____

FOOD LOG
STAGE 9 : DAY 5

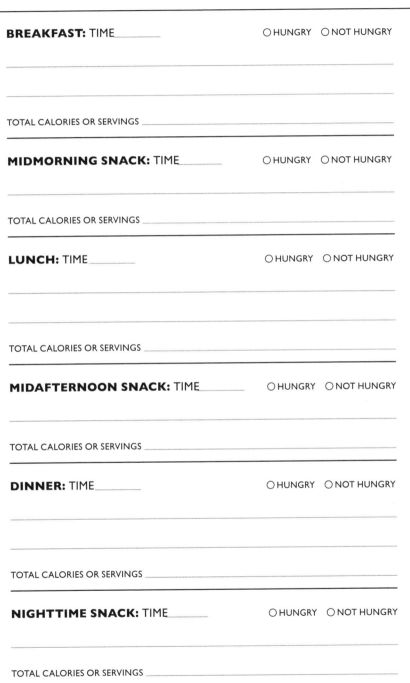

BREAKFAST: TIME_____   ○ HUNGRY   ○ NOT HUNGRY

_____

_____

TOTAL CALORIES OR SERVINGS _____

MIDMORNING SNACK: TIME_____   ○ HUNGRY   ○ NOT HUNGRY

_____

TOTAL CALORIES OR SERVINGS _____

LUNCH: TIME_____   ○ HUNGRY   ○ NOT HUNGRY

_____

_____

TOTAL CALORIES OR SERVINGS _____

MIDAFTERNOON SNACK: TIME_____   ○ HUNGRY   ○ NOT HUNGRY

_____

TOTAL CALORIES OR SERVINGS _____

DINNER: TIME_____   ○ HUNGRY   ○ NOT HUNGRY

_____

_____

TOTAL CALORIES OR SERVINGS _____

NIGHTTIME SNACK: TIME_____   ○ HUNGRY   ○ NOT HUNGRY

_____

TOTAL CALORIES OR SERVINGS _____

WORKOUT

STAGE 9 : DAY 6

DATE: _____

TIME WALKING: _____

TIME RUNNING: _____

TOTAL WORKOUT TIME: _____

COURSE: _____

_____

RATE HOW YOU FELT (1 being the worst and 10 being the best):

1   2   3   4   5   6   7   8   9   10

OTHER PHYSICAL ACTIVITY: _____

_____

NOTES (weather, injuries, etc.): _____

_____

_____

_____

_____

_____

_____

_____

FOOD LOG
STAGE 9 : DAY 6

BREAKFAST: TIME_____   ○ HUNGRY   ○ NOT HUNGRY

_____

_____

TOTAL CALORIES OR SERVINGS _____

MIDMORNING SNACK: TIME_____   ○ HUNGRY   ○ NOT HUNGRY

_____

TOTAL CALORIES OR SERVINGS _____

LUNCH: TIME_____   ○ HUNGRY   ○ NOT HUNGRY

_____

_____

TOTAL CALORIES OR SERVINGS _____

MIDAFTERNOON SNACK: TIME_____   ○ HUNGRY   ○ NOT HUNGRY

_____

TOTAL CALORIES OR SERVINGS _____

DINNER: TIME_____   ○ HUNGRY   ○ NOT HUNGRY

_____

_____

TOTAL CALORIES OR SERVINGS _____

NIGHTTIME SNACK: TIME_____   ○ HUNGRY   ○ NOT HUNGRY

_____

TOTAL CALORIES OR SERVINGS _____

Run Your Butt Off!

WORKOUT
STAGE 9 : DAY 7

DATE: _____

TIME WALKING: _____

TIME RUNNING: _____

TOTAL WORKOUT TIME: _____

COURSE: _____

_____

RATE HOW YOU FELT (1 being the worst and 10 being the best):

1   2   3   4   5   6   7   8   9   10

OTHER PHYSICAL ACTIVITY: _____

_____

NOTES (weather, injuries, etc.): _____

_____

_____

_____

_____

_____

_____

_____

FOOD LOG
STAGE 9 : DAY 7

BREAKFAST: TIME_____   ○ HUNGRY   ○ NOT HUNGRY

_____

_____

TOTAL CALORIES OR SERVINGS _____

MIDMORNING SNACK: TIME_____   ○ HUNGRY   ○ NOT HUNGRY

_____

TOTAL CALORIES OR SERVINGS _____

LUNCH: TIME_____   ○ HUNGRY   ○ NOT HUNGRY

_____

_____

TOTAL CALORIES OR SERVINGS _____

MIDAFTERNOON SNACK: TIME_____   ○ HUNGRY   ○ NOT HUNGRY

_____

TOTAL CALORIES OR SERVINGS _____

DINNER: TIME_____   ○ HUNGRY   ○ NOT HUNGRY

_____

_____

TOTAL CALORIES OR SERVINGS _____

NIGHTTIME SNACK: TIME_____   ○ HUNGRY   ○ NOT HUNGRY

_____

TOTAL CALORIES OR SERVINGS _____

Stage 9 CHECK-IN

WEIGHT_____

CHEST_____

WAIST_____

HIPS (AT FULLEST PART)_____

LEFT THIGH_____

RIGHT THIGH_____

LEFT BICEPS_____

RIGHT BICEPS_____

THOUGHTS ON THE WORKOUTS: Record the weather, your effort level, aches and pains, challenges, and successes. How hard did it feel?

_____

_____

_____

GOALS UPDATE

GOAL	DEADLINE FOR MEETING IT	MET GOAL/STILL IN PROGRESS

Stage 10

WORKOUT SUMMARY

- Walk for 2 minutes. Run for 13 minutes.
- Repeat that sequence one more time.
- End with 3 minutes of walking.

**Total workout time:
33 MINUTES, 26 of which are running**

Do this workout at least three or four times in a week
before moving on to the next stage.

**BUDD'S
BUZZ**

"My son is a competitive gymnast, and for years I've been
driving him to practice in the afternoons, dropping him
off, then going for a run. Most of the parents sit in the
bleachers to watch. I usually return about 10 minutes
before practice ends, and almost every time one of the
other parents will say to me, 'Oh, you're a runner? I wish
I had time to run.' That drives me crazy! If you've been
sitting here for an hour, you have time to run!"

DATE: _____

TIME WALKING: _____

TIME RUNNING: _____

TOTAL WORKOUT TIME: _____

COURSE: _____

_____

RATE HOW YOU FELT (1 being the worst and 10 being the best):

1   2   3   4   5   6   7   8   9   10

OTHER PHYSICAL ACTIVITY: _____

_____

NOTES (weather, injuries, etc.): _____

_____

_____

_____

_____

_____

_____

_____

FOOD LOG
STAGE 10 : DAY 1

BREAKFAST: TIME_____　　　　　　　○ HUNGRY　○ NOT HUNGRY

_____

_____

TOTAL CALORIES OR SERVINGS _____

MIDMORNING SNACK: TIME_____　　　○ HUNGRY　○ NOT HUNGRY

_____

TOTAL CALORIES OR SERVINGS _____

LUNCH: TIME_____　　　　　　　　　○ HUNGRY　○ NOT HUNGRY

_____

_____

TOTAL CALORIES OR SERVINGS _____

MIDAFTERNOON SNACK: TIME_____　○ HUNGRY　○ NOT HUNGRY

_____

TOTAL CALORIES OR SERVINGS _____

DINNER: TIME_____　　　　　　　　○ HUNGRY　○ NOT HUNGRY

_____

_____

TOTAL CALORIES OR SERVINGS _____

NIGHTTIME SNACK: TIME_____　　　○ HUNGRY　○ NOT HUNGRY

_____

TOTAL CALORIES OR SERVINGS _____

WORKOUT
STAGE 10 : DAY 2

DATE: _____

TIME WALKING: _____

TIME RUNNING: _____

TOTAL WORKOUT TIME: _____

COURSE: _____

_____

RATE HOW YOU FELT (1 being the worst and 10 being the best):

1   2   3   4   5   6   7   8   9   10

OTHER PHYSICAL ACTIVITY: _____

_____

NOTES (weather, injuries, etc.): _____

_____

_____

_____

_____

_____

_____

_____

FOOD LOG
STAGE 10 : DAY 2

BREAKFAST: TIME_____   ○ HUNGRY   ○ NOT HUNGRY

_____

_____

TOTAL CALORIES OR SERVINGS _____

MIDMORNING SNACK: TIME_____   ○ HUNGRY   ○ NOT HUNGRY

_____

TOTAL CALORIES OR SERVINGS _____

LUNCH: TIME_____   ○ HUNGRY   ○ NOT HUNGRY

_____

_____

TOTAL CALORIES OR SERVINGS _____

MIDAFTERNOON SNACK: TIME_____   ○ HUNGRY   ○ NOT HUNGRY

_____

TOTAL CALORIES OR SERVINGS _____

DINNER: TIME_____   ○ HUNGRY   ○ NOT HUNGRY

_____

_____

TOTAL CALORIES OR SERVINGS _____

NIGHTTIME SNACK: TIME_____   ○ HUNGRY   ○ NOT HUNGRY

_____

TOTAL CALORIES OR SERVINGS _____

WORKOUT
STAGE 10 : DAY 3

DATE: _____

TIME WALKING: _____

TIME RUNNING: _____

TOTAL WORKOUT TIME: _____

COURSE: _____

_____

RATE HOW YOU FELT (1 being the worst and 10 being the best):

1   2   3   4   5   6   7   8   9   10

OTHER PHYSICAL ACTIVITY: _____

_____

NOTES (weather, injuries, etc.): _____

_____

_____

_____

_____

_____

_____

_____

FOOD LOG
STAGE 10 : DAY 3

BREAKFAST: TIME_____   ○ HUNGRY   ○ NOT HUNGRY

_____

_____

TOTAL CALORIES OR SERVINGS _____

MIDMORNING SNACK: TIME_____   ○ HUNGRY   ○ NOT HUNGRY

_____

TOTAL CALORIES OR SERVINGS _____

LUNCH: TIME_____   ○ HUNGRY   ○ NOT HUNGRY

_____

_____

TOTAL CALORIES OR SERVINGS _____

MIDAFTERNOON SNACK: TIME_____   ○ HUNGRY   ○ NOT HUNGRY

_____

TOTAL CALORIES OR SERVINGS _____

DINNER: TIME_____   ○ HUNGRY   ○ NOT HUNGRY

_____

_____

TOTAL CALORIES OR SERVINGS _____

NIGHTTIME SNACK: TIME_____   ○ HUNGRY   ○ NOT HUNGRY

_____

TOTAL CALORIES OR SERVINGS _____

WORKOUT
STAGE 10 : DAY 4

DATE: _____

TIME WALKING: _____

TIME RUNNING: _____

TOTAL WORKOUT TIME: _____

COURSE: _____

_____

RATE HOW YOU FELT (1 being the worst and 10 being the best):

1   2   3   4   5   6   7   8   9   10

OTHER PHYSICAL ACTIVITY: _____

_____

NOTES (weather, injuries, etc.): _____

_____

_____

_____

_____

_____

_____

_____

FOOD LOG
STAGE 10 : DAY 4

BREAKFAST: TIME_____   ○ HUNGRY   ○ NOT HUNGRY

_____

_____

TOTAL CALORIES OR SERVINGS _____

MIDMORNING SNACK: TIME_____   ○ HUNGRY   ○ NOT HUNGRY

_____

TOTAL CALORIES OR SERVINGS _____

LUNCH: TIME_____   ○ HUNGRY   ○ NOT HUNGRY

_____

_____

TOTAL CALORIES OR SERVINGS _____

MIDAFTERNOON SNACK: TIME_____   ○ HUNGRY   ○ NOT HUNGRY

_____

TOTAL CALORIES OR SERVINGS _____

DINNER: TIME_____   ○ HUNGRY   ○ NOT HUNGRY

_____

_____

TOTAL CALORIES OR SERVINGS _____

NIGHTTIME SNACK: TIME_____   ○ HUNGRY   ○ NOT HUNGRY

_____

TOTAL CALORIES OR SERVINGS _____

Run Your Butt Off!

WORKOUT
STAGE 10 : DAY 5

DATE: _____

TIME WALKING: _____

TIME RUNNING: _____

TOTAL WORKOUT TIME: _____

COURSE: _____

_____

RATE HOW YOU FELT (1 being the worst and 10 being the best):

1   2   3   4   5   6   7   8   9   10

OTHER PHYSICAL ACTIVITY: _____

_____

NOTES (weather, injuries, etc.): _____

_____

_____

_____

_____

_____

_____

FOOD LOG
STAGE 10 : DAY 5

BREAKFAST: TIME_____   ○ HUNGRY   ○ NOT HUNGRY

_____

_____

TOTAL CALORIES OR SERVINGS _____

MIDMORNING SNACK: TIME_____   ○ HUNGRY   ○ NOT HUNGRY

_____

TOTAL CALORIES OR SERVINGS _____

LUNCH: TIME_____   ○ HUNGRY   ○ NOT HUNGRY

_____

_____

TOTAL CALORIES OR SERVINGS _____

MIDAFTERNOON SNACK: TIME_____   ○ HUNGRY   ○ NOT HUNGRY

_____

TOTAL CALORIES OR SERVINGS _____

DINNER: TIME_____   ○ HUNGRY   ○ NOT HUNGRY

_____

_____

TOTAL CALORIES OR SERVINGS _____

NIGHTTIME SNACK: TIME_____   ○ HUNGRY   ○ NOT HUNGRY

_____

TOTAL CALORIES OR SERVINGS _____

DATE: _____

TIME WALKING: _____

TIME RUNNING: _____

TOTAL WORKOUT TIME: _____

COURSE: _____

_____

RATE HOW YOU FELT (1 being the worst and 10 being the best):

1   2   3   4   5   6   7   8   9   10

OTHER PHYSICAL ACTIVITY: _____

_____

NOTES (weather, injuries, etc.): _____

_____

_____

_____

_____

_____

_____

_____

FOOD LOG
STAGE 10 : DAY 6

BREAKFAST: TIME_____   ○ HUNGRY   ○ NOT HUNGRY

_____

_____

TOTAL CALORIES OR SERVINGS _____

MIDMORNING SNACK: TIME_____   ○ HUNGRY   ○ NOT HUNGRY

_____

TOTAL CALORIES OR SERVINGS _____

LUNCH: TIME_____   ○ HUNGRY   ○ NOT HUNGRY

_____

_____

TOTAL CALORIES OR SERVINGS _____

MIDAFTERNOON SNACK: TIME_____   ○ HUNGRY   ○ NOT HUNGRY

_____

TOTAL CALORIES OR SERVINGS _____

DINNER: TIME_____   ○ HUNGRY   ○ NOT HUNGRY

_____

_____

TOTAL CALORIES OR SERVINGS _____

NIGHTTIME SNACK: TIME_____   ○ HUNGRY   ○ NOT HUNGRY

_____

TOTAL CALORIES OR SERVINGS _____

DATE: _____

TIME WALKING: _____

TIME RUNNING: _____

TOTAL WORKOUT TIME: _____

COURSE: _____

_____

RATE HOW YOU FELT (1 being the worst and 10 being the best):

1   2   3   4   5   6   7   8   9   10

OTHER PHYSICAL ACTIVITY: _____

_____

NOTES (weather, injuries, etc.): _____

_____

_____

_____

_____

_____

_____

_____

_____

FOOD LOG
STAGE 10 : DAY 7

BREAKFAST: TIME_____   ○ HUNGRY   ○ NOT HUNGRY

_____

_____

TOTAL CALORIES OR SERVINGS _____

MIDMORNING SNACK: TIME_____   ○ HUNGRY   ○ NOT HUNGRY

_____

TOTAL CALORIES OR SERVINGS _____

LUNCH: TIME_____   ○ HUNGRY   ○ NOT HUNGRY

_____

_____

TOTAL CALORIES OR SERVINGS _____

MIDAFTERNOON SNACK: TIME_____   ○ HUNGRY   ○ NOT HUNGRY

_____

TOTAL CALORIES OR SERVINGS _____

DINNER: TIME_____   ○ HUNGRY   ○ NOT HUNGRY

_____

_____

TOTAL CALORIES OR SERVINGS _____

NIGHTTIME SNACK: TIME_____   ○ HUNGRY   ○ NOT HUNGRY

_____

TOTAL CALORIES OR SERVINGS _____

Stage 10 CHECK-IN

WEIGHT_____

CHEST_____

WAIST_____

HIPS (AT FULLEST PART)_____

LEFT THIGH_____

RIGHT THIGH_____

LEFT BICEPS_____

RIGHT BICEPS_____

THOUGHTS ON THE WORKOUTS: Record the weather, your effort level, aches and pains, challenges, and successes. How hard did it feel?

_____

_____

_____

GOALS UPDATE

GOAL	DEADLINE FOR MEETING IT	MET GOAL/STILL IN PROGRESS

Stage 11

WORKOUT SUMMARY

- Walk for 2 minutes. Run for 14 minutes.
- Then walk for 1 minute. Run for 14 minutes.
- End with 3 minutes of walking.

Total workout time:
34 MINUTES, 28 of which are running

Do this workout at least three or four times in a week before moving on to the final stage.

BUDD'S BUZZ

"It's always a help if you can plan to meet a friend for a workout. While a running friend can be integral to your success, you don't have to run every step side by side. The running relationship is beneficial in so many other ways: for the motivation, for the friendly face, for the high five at the end, and for the common understanding of what you're trying to accomplish. The best thing you can say if you're significantly slower is, 'Look, we'll meet, we'll go for the run, but you're faster than I am, so just go ahead. I'm out here, I'm good, and we'll meet up at the finish.'"

WORKOUT
STAGE II : DAY I

DATE: _____

TIME WALKING: _____

TIME RUNNING: _____

TOTAL WORKOUT TIME: _____

COURSE: _____

_____

RATE HOW YOU FELT (I being the worst and 10 being the best):

1	2	3	4	5	6	7	8	9	10

OTHER PHYSICAL ACTIVITY: _____

_____

NOTES (weather, injuries, etc.): _____

_____

_____

_____

_____

_____

_____

_____

FOOD LOG
STAGE II : DAY I

BREAKFAST: TIME_____   ○ HUNGRY   ○ NOT HUNGRY

_____

_____

TOTAL CALORIES OR SERVINGS _____

MIDMORNING SNACK: TIME_____   ○ HUNGRY   ○ NOT HUNGRY

_____

TOTAL CALORIES OR SERVINGS _____

LUNCH: TIME_____   ○ HUNGRY   ○ NOT HUNGRY

_____

_____

TOTAL CALORIES OR SERVINGS _____

MIDAFTERNOON SNACK: TIME_____   ○ HUNGRY   ○ NOT HUNGRY

_____

TOTAL CALORIES OR SERVINGS _____

DINNER: TIME_____   ○ HUNGRY   ○ NOT HUNGRY

_____

_____

TOTAL CALORIES OR SERVINGS _____

NIGHTTIME SNACK: TIME_____   ○ HUNGRY   ○ NOT HUNGRY

_____

TOTAL CALORIES OR SERVINGS _____

WORKOUT
STAGE 11 : DAY 2

DATE: _____

TIME WALKING: _____

TIME RUNNING: _____

TOTAL WORKOUT TIME: _____

COURSE: _____

_____

RATE HOW YOU FELT (1 being the worst and 10 being the best):

1   2   3   4   5   6   7   8   9   10

OTHER PHYSICAL ACTIVITY: _____

_____

NOTES (weather, injuries, etc.): _____

_____

_____

_____

_____

_____

_____

_____

FOOD LOG
STAGE II : DAY 2

BREAKFAST: TIME_____   ○ HUNGRY   ○ NOT HUNGRY

_____

_____

TOTAL CALORIES OR SERVINGS _____

MIDMORNING SNACK: TIME_____   ○ HUNGRY   ○ NOT HUNGRY

_____

TOTAL CALORIES OR SERVINGS _____

LUNCH: TIME_____   ○ HUNGRY   ○ NOT HUNGRY

_____

_____

TOTAL CALORIES OR SERVINGS _____

MIDAFTERNOON SNACK: TIME_____   ○ HUNGRY   ○ NOT HUNGRY

_____

TOTAL CALORIES OR SERVINGS _____

DINNER: TIME_____   ○ HUNGRY   ○ NOT HUNGRY

_____

_____

TOTAL CALORIES OR SERVINGS _____

NIGHTTIME SNACK: TIME_____   ○ HUNGRY   ○ NOT HUNGRY

_____

TOTAL CALORIES OR SERVINGS _____

DATE: _____

TIME WALKING: _____

TIME RUNNING: _____

TOTAL WORKOUT TIME: _____

COURSE: _____

_____

RATE HOW YOU FELT (1 being the worst and 10 being the best):

1   2   3   4   5   6   7   8   9   10

OTHER PHYSICAL ACTIVITY: _____

_____

NOTES (weather, injuries, etc.): _____

_____

_____

_____

_____

_____

_____

FOOD LOG
STAGE II : DAY 3

BREAKFAST: TIME_____   ○ HUNGRY   ○ NOT HUNGRY

_____

_____

TOTAL CALORIES OR SERVINGS _____

MIDMORNING SNACK: TIME_____   ○ HUNGRY   ○ NOT HUNGRY

_____

TOTAL CALORIES OR SERVINGS _____

LUNCH: TIME_____   ○ HUNGRY   ○ NOT HUNGRY

_____

_____

TOTAL CALORIES OR SERVINGS _____

MIDAFTERNOON SNACK: TIME_____   ○ HUNGRY   ○ NOT HUNGRY

_____

TOTAL CALORIES OR SERVINGS _____

DINNER: TIME_____   ○ HUNGRY   ○ NOT HUNGRY

_____

_____

TOTAL CALORIES OR SERVINGS _____

NIGHTTIME SNACK: TIME_____   ○ HUNGRY   ○ NOT HUNGRY

_____

TOTAL CALORIES OR SERVINGS _____

WORKOUT
STAGE 11 : DAY 4

DATE: _____

TIME WALKING: _____

TIME RUNNING: _____

TOTAL WORKOUT TIME: _____

COURSE: _____

_____

RATE HOW YOU FELT (1 being the worst and 10 being the best):

1   2   3   4   5   6   7   8   9   10

OTHER PHYSICAL ACTIVITY: _____

_____

NOTES (weather, injuries, etc.): _____

_____

_____

_____

_____

_____

_____

FOOD LOG
STAGE II : DAY 4

BREAKFAST: TIME_____   ○ HUNGRY   ○ NOT HUNGRY

_____

_____

TOTAL CALORIES OR SERVINGS _____

MIDMORNING SNACK: TIME_____   ○ HUNGRY   ○ NOT HUNGRY

_____

TOTAL CALORIES OR SERVINGS _____

LUNCH: TIME_____   ○ HUNGRY   ○ NOT HUNGRY

_____

_____

TOTAL CALORIES OR SERVINGS _____

MIDAFTERNOON SNACK: TIME_____   ○ HUNGRY   ○ NOT HUNGRY

_____

TOTAL CALORIES OR SERVINGS _____

DINNER: TIME_____   ○ HUNGRY   ○ NOT HUNGRY

_____

_____

TOTAL CALORIES OR SERVINGS _____

NIGHTTIME SNACK: TIME_____   ○ HUNGRY   ○ NOT HUNGRY

_____

TOTAL CALORIES OR SERVINGS _____

WORKOUT
STAGE 11 : DAY 5

DATE: _____

TIME WALKING: _____

TIME RUNNING: _____

TOTAL WORKOUT TIME: _____

COURSE: _____

_____

RATE HOW YOU FELT (1 being the worst and 10 being the best):

1   2   3   4   5   6   7   8   9   10

OTHER PHYSICAL ACTIVITY: _____

_____

NOTES (weather, injuries, etc.): _____

_____

_____

_____

_____

_____

_____

_____

FOOD LOG
STAGE II : DAY 5

BREAKFAST: TIME_____   ○ HUNGRY   ○ NOT HUNGRY

_____

_____

TOTAL CALORIES OR SERVINGS _____

MIDMORNING SNACK: TIME_____   ○ HUNGRY   ○ NOT HUNGRY

_____

TOTAL CALORIES OR SERVINGS _____

LUNCH: TIME_____   ○ HUNGRY   ○ NOT HUNGRY

_____

_____

TOTAL CALORIES OR SERVINGS _____

MIDAFTERNOON SNACK: TIME_____   ○ HUNGRY   ○ NOT HUNGRY

_____

TOTAL CALORIES OR SERVINGS _____

DINNER: TIME_____   ○ HUNGRY   ○ NOT HUNGRY

_____

_____

TOTAL CALORIES OR SERVINGS _____

NIGHTTIME SNACK: TIME_____   ○ HUNGRY   ○ NOT HUNGRY

_____

TOTAL CALORIES OR SERVINGS _____

Run Your Butt Off!

WORKOUT
STAGE 11 : DAY 6

DATE: _____

TIME WALKING: _____

TIME RUNNING: _____

TOTAL WORKOUT TIME: _____

COURSE: _____

_____

RATE HOW YOU FELT (1 being the worst and 10 being the best):

1   2   3   4   5   6   7   8   9   10

OTHER PHYSICAL ACTIVITY: _____

_____

NOTES (weather, injuries, etc.): _____

_____

_____

_____

_____

_____

_____

_____

FOOD LOG
STAGE II : DAY 6

BREAKFAST: TIME_____   ○ HUNGRY ○ NOT HUNGRY

_____

_____

TOTAL CALORIES OR SERVINGS _____

MIDMORNING SNACK: TIME_____   ○ HUNGRY ○ NOT HUNGRY

_____

TOTAL CALORIES OR SERVINGS _____

LUNCH: TIME_____   ○ HUNGRY ○ NOT HUNGRY

_____

_____

TOTAL CALORIES OR SERVINGS _____

MIDAFTERNOON SNACK: TIME_____   ○ HUNGRY ○ NOT HUNGRY

_____

TOTAL CALORIES OR SERVINGS _____

DINNER: TIME_____   ○ HUNGRY ○ NOT HUNGRY

_____

_____

TOTAL CALORIES OR SERVINGS _____

NIGHTTIME SNACK: TIME_____   ○ HUNGRY ○ NOT HUNGRY

_____

TOTAL CALORIES OR SERVINGS _____

WORKOUT
STAGE 11 : DAY 7

DATE: _____

TIME WALKING: _____

TIME RUNNING: _____

TOTAL WORKOUT TIME: _____

COURSE: _____

_____

RATE HOW YOU FELT (1 being the worst and 10 being the best):

1   2   3   4   5   6   7   8   9   10

OTHER PHYSICAL ACTIVITY: _____

_____

NOTES (weather, injuries, etc.): _____

_____

_____

_____

_____

_____

_____

_____

FOOD LOG
STAGE II : DAY 7

BREAKFAST: TIME_____   ○ HUNGRY   ○ NOT HUNGRY

_____

_____

TOTAL CALORIES OR SERVINGS _____

MIDMORNING SNACK: TIME_____   ○ HUNGRY   ○ NOT HUNGRY

_____

TOTAL CALORIES OR SERVINGS _____

LUNCH: TIME_____   ○ HUNGRY   ○ NOT HUNGRY

_____

_____

TOTAL CALORIES OR SERVINGS _____

MIDAFTERNOON SNACK: TIME_____   ○ HUNGRY   ○ NOT HUNGRY

_____

TOTAL CALORIES OR SERVINGS _____

DINNER: TIME_____   ○ HUNGRY   ○ NOT HUNGRY

_____

_____

TOTAL CALORIES OR SERVINGS _____

NIGHTTIME SNACK: TIME_____   ○ HUNGRY   ○ NOT HUNGRY

_____

TOTAL CALORIES OR SERVINGS _____

Stage 11 CHECK-IN

WEIGHT_____

CHEST_____

WAIST_____

HIPS (AT FULLEST PART)_____

LEFT THIGH_____

RIGHT THIGH_____

LEFT BICEPS_____

RIGHT BICEPS_____

THOUGHTS ON THE WORKOUTS: Record the weather, your effort level, aches and pains, challenges, and successes. How hard did it feel?

_____

_____

GOALS UPDATE

GOAL	DEADLINE FOR MEETING IT	MET GOAL/STILL IN PROGRESS

Stage 12

WORKOUT SUMMARY

• Walk for 3 minutes (or until you're good and ready).

• Run for 30 minutes.

• End with 3 minutes of walking.

**Total workout time:
36 MINUTES, 30 of which are running**

Repeat this sequence throughout your whole life.

BUDD'S BUZZ

"For beginners going from 14 minutes to 30 minutes, it's all mental. One hundred percent mental. I hear it all the time. They'll say, 'I've only been running 13, 14 minutes—how can I run all the way to 30?' I explain to them that the 1-minute break they've been taking is like nothing. A 2-minute break is nothing.

"If they're not convinced, I tell them this: 'If you get to 19 minutes and you want to stop for a minute, go ahead.' But no one ever stops. You watch them and they get this look on their faces like 'I'm going to do this.' They are determined. They all have attitudes—if not to start with, then by the end."

DATE: _____

TIME WALKING: _____

TIME RUNNING: _____

TOTAL WORKOUT TIME: _____

COURSE: _____

_____

RATE HOW YOU FELT (1 being the worst and 10 being the best):

1   2   3   4   5   6   7   8   9   10

OTHER PHYSICAL ACTIVITY: _____

_____

NOTES (weather, injuries, etc.): _____

_____

_____

_____

_____

_____

_____

_____

FOOD LOG
STAGE 12 : DAY 1

BREAKFAST: TIME_____   ○ HUNGRY   ○ NOT HUNGRY

_____

_____

TOTAL CALORIES OR SERVINGS _____

MIDMORNING SNACK: TIME_____   ○ HUNGRY   ○ NOT HUNGRY

_____

TOTAL CALORIES OR SERVINGS _____

LUNCH: TIME_____   ○ HUNGRY   ○ NOT HUNGRY

_____

_____

TOTAL CALORIES OR SERVINGS _____

MIDAFTERNOON SNACK: TIME_____   ○ HUNGRY   ○ NOT HUNGRY

_____

TOTAL CALORIES OR SERVINGS _____

DINNER: TIME_____   ○ HUNGRY   ○ NOT HUNGRY

_____

_____

TOTAL CALORIES OR SERVINGS _____

NIGHTTIME SNACK: TIME_____   ○ HUNGRY   ○ NOT HUNGRY

_____

TOTAL CALORIES OR SERVINGS _____

WORKOUT
STAGE 12 : DAY 2

DATE: _____

TIME WALKING: _____

TIME RUNNING: _____

TOTAL WORKOUT TIME: _____

COURSE: _____

_____

RATE HOW YOU FELT (1 being the worst and 10 being the best):

1   2   3   4   5   6   7   8   9   10

OTHER PHYSICAL ACTIVITY: _____

_____

NOTES (weather, injuries, etc.): _____

_____

_____

_____

_____

_____

_____

_____

FOOD LOG
STAGE 12 : DAY 2

BREAKFAST: TIME_____   ○ HUNGRY   ○ NOT HUNGRY

_____

_____

TOTAL CALORIES OR SERVINGS _____

MIDMORNING SNACK: TIME_____   ○ HUNGRY   ○ NOT HUNGRY

_____

TOTAL CALORIES OR SERVINGS _____

LUNCH: TIME_____   ○ HUNGRY   ○ NOT HUNGRY

_____

_____

TOTAL CALORIES OR SERVINGS _____

MIDAFTERNOON SNACK: TIME_____   ○ HUNGRY   ○ NOT HUNGRY

_____

TOTAL CALORIES OR SERVINGS _____

DINNER: TIME_____   ○ HUNGRY   ○ NOT HUNGRY

_____

_____

TOTAL CALORIES OR SERVINGS _____

NIGHTTIME SNACK: TIME_____   ○ HUNGRY   ○ NOT HUNGRY

_____

TOTAL CALORIES OR SERVINGS _____

WORKOUT
STAGE 12 : DAY 3

DATE: _____

TIME WALKING: _____

TIME RUNNING: _____

TOTAL WORKOUT TIME: _____

COURSE: _____

_____

RATE HOW YOU FELT (1 being the worst and 10 being the best):

1   2   3   4   5   6   7   8   9   10

OTHER PHYSICAL ACTIVITY: _____

_____

NOTES (weather, injuries, etc.): _____

_____

_____

_____

_____

_____

_____

_____

FOOD LOG
STAGE 12 : DAY 3

BREAKFAST: TIME_____   ○ HUNGRY   ○ NOT HUNGRY

_____

_____

TOTAL CALORIES OR SERVINGS _____

MIDMORNING SNACK: TIME_____   ○ HUNGRY   ○ NOT HUNGRY

_____

TOTAL CALORIES OR SERVINGS _____

LUNCH: TIME_____   ○ HUNGRY   ○ NOT HUNGRY

_____

_____

TOTAL CALORIES OR SERVINGS _____

MIDAFTERNOON SNACK: TIME_____   ○ HUNGRY   ○ NOT HUNGRY

_____

TOTAL CALORIES OR SERVINGS _____

DINNER: TIME_____   ○ HUNGRY   ○ NOT HUNGRY

_____

_____

TOTAL CALORIES OR SERVINGS _____

NIGHTTIME SNACK: TIME_____   ○ HUNGRY   ○ NOT HUNGRY

_____

TOTAL CALORIES OR SERVINGS _____

WORKOUT
STAGE 12 : DAY 4

DATE: _____

TIME WALKING: _____

TIME RUNNING: _____

TOTAL WORKOUT TIME: _____

COURSE: _____
_____

RATE HOW YOU FELT (1 being the worst and 10 being the best):

1   2   3   4   5   6   7   8   9   10

OTHER PHYSICAL ACTIVITY: _____
_____

NOTES (weather, injuries, etc.): _____
_____
_____
_____
_____
_____
_____
_____

FOOD LOG
STAGE 12 : DAY 4

BREAKFAST: TIME_____   ○ HUNGRY   ○ NOT HUNGRY

_____

_____

TOTAL CALORIES OR SERVINGS _____

MIDMORNING SNACK: TIME_____   ○ HUNGRY   ○ NOT HUNGRY

_____

TOTAL CALORIES OR SERVINGS _____

LUNCH: TIME_____   ○ HUNGRY   ○ NOT HUNGRY

_____

_____

TOTAL CALORIES OR SERVINGS _____

MIDAFTERNOON SNACK: TIME_____   ○ HUNGRY   ○ NOT HUNGRY

_____

TOTAL CALORIES OR SERVINGS _____

DINNER: TIME_____   ○ HUNGRY   ○ NOT HUNGRY

_____

_____

TOTAL CALORIES OR SERVINGS _____

NIGHTTIME SNACK: TIME_____   ○ HUNGRY   ○ NOT HUNGRY

_____

TOTAL CALORIES OR SERVINGS _____

DATE: _____

TIME WALKING: _____

TIME RUNNING: _____

TOTAL WORKOUT TIME: _____

COURSE: _____

_____

RATE HOW YOU FELT (I being the worst and 10 being the best):

1   2   3   4   5   6   7   8   9   10

OTHER PHYSICAL ACTIVITY: _____

_____

NOTES (weather, injuries, etc.): _____

_____

_____

_____

_____

_____

_____

_____

FOOD LOG
STAGE 12 : DAY 5

BREAKFAST: TIME_____   ○ HUNGRY   ○ NOT HUNGRY

_____

_____

TOTAL CALORIES OR SERVINGS _____

MIDMORNING SNACK: TIME_____   ○ HUNGRY   ○ NOT HUNGRY

_____

TOTAL CALORIES OR SERVINGS _____

LUNCH: TIME_____   ○ HUNGRY   ○ NOT HUNGRY

_____

_____

TOTAL CALORIES OR SERVINGS _____

MIDAFTERNOON SNACK: TIME_____   ○ HUNGRY   ○ NOT HUNGRY

_____

TOTAL CALORIES OR SERVINGS _____

DINNER: TIME_____   ○ HUNGRY   ○ NOT HUNGRY

_____

_____

TOTAL CALORIES OR SERVINGS _____

NIGHTTIME SNACK: TIME_____   ○ HUNGRY   ○ NOT HUNGRY

_____

TOTAL CALORIES OR SERVINGS _____

WORKOUT
STAGE 12 : DAY 6

DATE: _____

TIME WALKING: _____

TIME RUNNING: _____

TOTAL WORKOUT TIME: _____

COURSE: _____

_____

RATE HOW YOU FELT (1 being the worst and 10 being the best):

1   2   3   4   5   6   7   8   9   10

OTHER PHYSICAL ACTIVITY: _____

_____

NOTES (weather, injuries, etc.): _____

_____

_____

_____

_____

_____

_____

_____

FOOD LOG
STAGE 12 : DAY 6

BREAKFAST: TIME_____   ○ HUNGRY   ○ NOT HUNGRY

_____

_____

TOTAL CALORIES OR SERVINGS _____

MIDMORNING SNACK: TIME_____   ○ HUNGRY   ○ NOT HUNGRY

_____

TOTAL CALORIES OR SERVINGS _____

LUNCH: TIME_____   ○ HUNGRY   ○ NOT HUNGRY

_____

_____

TOTAL CALORIES OR SERVINGS _____

MIDAFTERNOON SNACK: TIME_____   ○ HUNGRY   ○ NOT HUNGRY

_____

TOTAL CALORIES OR SERVINGS _____

DINNER: TIME_____   ○ HUNGRY   ○ NOT HUNGRY

_____

_____

TOTAL CALORIES OR SERVINGS _____

NIGHTTIME SNACK: TIME_____   ○ HUNGRY   ○ NOT HUNGRY

_____

TOTAL CALORIES OR SERVINGS _____

WORKOUT
STAGE 12 : DAY 7

DATE: _____

TIME WALKING: _____

TIME RUNNING: _____

TOTAL WORKOUT TIME: _____

COURSE: _____

_____

RATE HOW YOU FELT (1 being the worst and 10 being the best):

1   2   3   4   5   6   7   8   9   10

OTHER PHYSICAL ACTIVITY: _____

_____

NOTES (weather, injuries, etc.): _____

_____

_____

_____

_____

_____

_____

_____

FOOD LOG
STAGE 12 : DAY 7

BREAKFAST: TIME_____   ○ HUNGRY   ○ NOT HUNGRY

_____

_____

TOTAL CALORIES OR SERVINGS _____

MIDMORNING SNACK: TIME_____   ○ HUNGRY   ○ NOT HUNGRY

_____

TOTAL CALORIES OR SERVINGS _____

LUNCH: TIME_____   ○ HUNGRY   ○ NOT HUNGRY

_____

_____

TOTAL CALORIES OR SERVINGS _____

MIDAFTERNOON SNACK: TIME_____   ○ HUNGRY   ○ NOT HUNGRY

_____

TOTAL CALORIES OR SERVINGS _____

DINNER: TIME_____   ○ HUNGRY   ○ NOT HUNGRY

_____

_____

TOTAL CALORIES OR SERVINGS _____

NIGHTTIME SNACK: TIME_____   ○ HUNGRY   ○ NOT HUNGRY

_____

TOTAL CALORIES OR SERVINGS _____

Stage 12 FINAL CHECK-IN

You've made it through Stage 12 and completed the Run Your Butt Off! program. Flip back to page 27 and write in your starting stats. Then take your latest measurements. Have you reached your goals? Even if you have a way to go, you are now an athlete and can keep running toward that finish line. On the next page, take a moment to update your goals from page 28.

	TODAY	STARTING STATS
HEIGHT		
WEIGHT		
BODY MASS INDEX (BMI)*		
CHEST		
WAIST		
HIPS (AT FULLEST PART)		
LEFT THIGH		
RIGHT THIGH		
LEFT BICEPS		
RIGHT BICEPS		

THOUGHTS ON THE WORKOUTS: Record the weather, your effort level, aches and pains, challenges, and successes. How hard did it feel?

_____

_____

_____

GOALS UPDATE

Look back at your goals from 12 weeks ago. Have you accomplished everything you set out to do? How can you keep going toward those longer-term goals? This is also a great place to make some new promises to yourself. Will you run a 5-K or a half-marathon? Make a distance or speed goal? Think about where you'd like to be in another 12 weeks from today.

GOAL	DEADLINE FOR MEETING IT	MET GOAL/STILL IN PROGRESS

Congratulations!

You're a runner—welcome to the club! There are a few more things the RYBO team can teach you now that you've worked your way up to running for 30 minutes. Here are three approaches you can take to continue training and goal setting. Don't forget to check out Chapter 12 in your copy of *Run Your Butt Off!* for more details!

GET READY FOR RACE DAY

Give yourself a pat on the back—if you haven't already tried one, you're now definitely qualified to attempt a 5-K. It's normal to feel some jitters when you run your first race, but it's a great goal to keep you moving. Remember the following quick pointers for getting to your first finish line:

➤ Don't try anything unusual for breakfast the morning of the race. Stick to your old routine. You know what works. Ditto for avoiding new shoes, new shorts, new shirts. Go for the tried-and-true.

➤ Line up about three-quarters of the way back in the pack, so you're behind the speedy guys in singlets and don't get mowed over. But get ahead of the people who are walking the entire way. You can usually tell by the footwear who's been training and who's out for a walk.

➤ Start out conservatively, even a little slower than your training pace. The goal is to finish your first race happy and upright, and you won't be either of those things if you start out so fast that you've used up all your energy in the first mile. Ignore the pack and set your own pace. After the first mile, if you want to step it up just a wee bit, that's fine. You can speed up slightly again at the 2-mile mark if you feel like you're bursting with energy.

➤ Put a smile on your face as you cross the finish line. You've just done something incredible, so look the part!

GO LONG!

In the coming weeks, we hope that 30 minutes of running will become easy for you. But it might take a while to get there. So going forward, try to organize your week around the principle of "going long" 1 day. Most people have more time for that on the weekend, both for the workout and for a little extra chilling out afterward. More experienced runners adapt a week-day run that's fairly routine, then push a little longer on the weekends. For instance, you could run 4 to 5 miles on Monday, Wednesday, and Friday, and then try for a longer run—maybe 8 miles—either Saturday or Sunday.

If that sounds daunting now, don't forget it's okay to take it slow. Start by finding a weekday workout you can live with. Maybe you alternate 2 minutes of walking with 8 minutes of running for 30 minutes during the week. Then perhaps your weekend run is the 30 minutes nonstop. In time, 30 minutes nonstop will feel routine and can become your weekday run.

Try to push yourself week by week, little by little. Don't settle into a comfortable groove for the long haul; after all, we wouldn't want you to get bored and stop running altogether!

LIFE IN THE FAST LANE

You're not ready to move up in distance, but you want to knock some time off the clock? See that finishing time a few minutes faster? If your 30-minute runs feel stale, try a speed workout once per week. Here are two workouts to try:

Workout 1

➤ Run at your normal pace for the first 10 minutes.

➤ Pick up the pace for 10 minutes to a harder effort level. Instead of being able to speak in complete sentences, you're breathing more heavily, so you're able to get out only three or four words at a time. It's a faster pace, but you're in control. You don't want to push so hard that you feel like you want to fall over exhausted after the 10 minutes are finished.

➤ Finish by running at your normal pace for the last 10 minutes.

Workout 2

➤ Run at your normal pace for the first 10 minutes.

➤ Alternate 1 minute of hard running with 1 minute of easy running for the next 10 minutes. You should feel a noticeable change in pace for the minute-long hard segments, but they shouldn't be so fast that you can't complete 5 of them.

➤ Finish by running at your normal pace for the last 10 minutes.

Workout 1 is an introduction to tempo running, and Workout 2 is a basic interval workout. These types of runs are staples of competitive runners' routines. You can learn more about them at runnersworld.com.